KEYS TO A MAGIC DOOR

ISAAC LEIB PERETZ

Keys to a Magic Door

SYLVIA ROTHCHILD

illustrated by
BERNARD KRIGSTEIN

FARRAR, STRAUS & CUDAHY
JEWISH PUBLICATION SOCIETY

To my children
ALICE, JUDY, and JOE

Contents

Author's Note

Isaac Leib Peretz was a great Jewish writer who lived in Poland from 1852 to 1915. He wrote hundreds of beautiful stories that delighted the people of his own time and are still precious today.

Peretz, however, was much more than a writer. He was an extraordinary teacher, a great lawyer, and both a leader and a servant of the Jewish people. Students, writers, and working people came from all over Europe to ask his advice and benefit from his wisdom.

In 1912, Peretz began to write the story of his life. He thought it would be a key to his work and that it would be easier to understand his stories if one knew what kind of a person he was, where he came from and how he lived. Though he did not live long enough to finish it, Peretz managed to leave not one key, but a whole collection of keys that can open many doors for us. In his book of *Memories* he described his schoolboy adventures; the escapades he shared with other boys his own age and his own special problems as a "young genius." His volumes of stories, poems, plays and articles open a door on the Jewish world of eastern Europe. Hitler destroyed that world completely but its towns and its people remain alive in Peretz's stories. In folk and fairy tales, he wrote about all the secret wishes and dreams of his people.

Peretz wrote in Yiddish, though he knew Hebrew, Polish, Russian and had even read French and English books. He chose Yiddish because at that time it was the only language that was understood by almost all Jews over the world. He wanted to speak to all of them, to the women with little schooling and to the men with good educations, to the rich and poor, to the merchants and the working people. In his skillful hands, Yiddish became poetical and dramatic, a language in which all feelings could be expressed and all thoughts explained. Peretz's stories have been translated into many languages, including English, but they are at their best in the original Yiddish.

Choose a key from the collection Peretz left for us and it will open a door to the past. One turn— and we are back in a world where most Jewish grandparents grew up. It seems strange to us, but it's familiar to them. It's very much like the place they once called home.

The material for this book was gathered from the *Complete Works* by I. L. Peretz, *Peretz* by Samuel Charney, *Letters and Speeches of I. L. Peretz,* edited by Nachman Meisel, *Peretz, the Psychologist of Literature,* by A. A. Roback, *Prince of the Ghetto,* by Maurice Samuel, *Peretz,* by Sol Liptzin and *In This World And the Next,* translated by Moshe Spiegel.

KEYS TO A MAGIC DOOR

RESPECT!

1

Schooldays in Zamosh

Yudele and Rivele Peretz lived in Zamosh, a Polish town of about five thousand people. In the summer of 1863 their oldest son Isaac studied with Reb Berishel just as he did in the winter. At seven in the morning he ran down the narrow, cobblestoned street to his teacher's small, one-room house with a high window that let little light into the room.

Thick blobs of wax dripped from the candles to the rough wooden table. Isaac and the other boys chanted their Hebrew lesson together while Reb Berishel watched to make sure they paid attention.

Henya, Reb Berishel's wife, sat in front of the fireplace, knitting. A fat red cat slept on the ledge over the oven.

Isaac moved his lips with the others although he was ten pages ahead of them. He remembered everything he read without any effort and he hated to repeat the familiar words over and over. Whenever Reb Berishel looked away, Isaac scraped some soft wax from the table. He shaped it into a ball and then into a bird. He added another bit of wax and turned the bird into a dog.

"Let me see," whispered the boy next to him.

"Let me see too," said Reb Berishel crossly. "What treasure are you hiding there from me?"

Isaac's face turned pink. He bit his lip and clenched his fist around the smooth wax figure.

"Come now," said his teacher, "what does our genius have for us today?"

The boys began to giggle. Isaac gave the dog to his teacher.

"What shall we do with him, Henya?" shouted Reb Berishel, as if his wife could tell him. "He could read the Bible when he was three years old. Now he's 11 and plays all day!" The dog was thrown into the fireplace.

Reb Berishel tapped his switch threateningly

and the children put innocent looks on their faces. It became so peaceful that the rhythm of the chant and the warmth of the half-dark room put Henya to sleep. The knitting slipped from her fingers to the floor. The cat jumped to catch it. In a minute the yarn was tangled around the legs of the chair and the table. The cat and the ball disappeared under a rickety bed in the corner of the room.

The children broke into laughter, Isaac's voice above all the others.

"Respect!" demanded Reb Berishel. "Where is your respect for your elders? If not Talmud, I'll teach you manners!" The switch came down on Isaac's fingers.

The boys groaned for him. Henya jumped as if to rescue him, but Reb Berishel glared at them all. He was very tired and his boys gave him a hard time. They were restless in summer and even worse in winter. When it was cold they would pour water on his doorstep, let it freeze and cover it with snow. Poor Reb Berishel was always falling in and out of his house. One day he complained that Henya brewed his tea too weak. One of the boys obligingly threw a lump of tar into the teapot to darken it.

"Such nice strong tea," said Reb Berishel and took the glass to his lips. Isaac stopped him from drinking, afraid that his teacher might get poisoned, but Isaac also took the punishment for knowing that there was tar in the teapot. Reb Berishel had many unhappy memories. One afternoon he had dozed off in the middle of a lesson for just a second. He woke to find that the tip of his beard had been glued to the table with candle wax. It was easy to blame Isaac, who had a bad habit of asking questions that were too hard to answer. Reb Berishel often found himself looking into Isaac's bright eyes, then, hemming and hawing, he would finally change the subject, only to have the question repeated another day.

It was not that he wasn't fond of his brightest student. Reb Berishel just couldn't keep up with the boy's restlessness and his quick mind. The teacher was as relieved as his pupils when the week ended.

Friday was a half-day at school. Isaac and his friend Yechezkel raced down to the square to watch a parade of Russian soldiers. A band was playing. The soldiers in red and gold tunics rode magnificent white horses. The boys stood on the steps of the courthouse and watched with open mouths.

A soldier came up behind them so quietly that they both jumped when he spoke. "We're off to the Turkish war, boys," he said. "How about coming along with us?" There was a twinkle in his eye, but the boys were too startled to notice it.

"God forbid!" said Isaac.

"You mean you wouldn't like a fine horse and a sharp sword?" asked the soldier in Polish, so the boys could understand a little. "What kind of boys are you?"

"I'd like the horse," said Yechezkel timidly.

"You may keep your horse and sword," said Isaac. "Our Torah teaches, thou shalt not kill."

"We're only killing some Turks," the soldier said playfully, stabbing Isaac with his finger.

"The Turks have done me no harm," said Isaac.

"No matter," said the soldier. "They're taking boys like you now. You'll see. You'll soldier with us in the Russian army."

"I live in Poland, not in Russia," said Isaac stubbornly.

"But Russia is the master. You'll go when they come for you."

"And if I refuse to go?" asked Isaac.

"They might . . . beat you," said the soldier.

"They can't beat everyone."

"They might . . . put you in chains," said the soldier with a smile.

"I'm not afraid," said Isaac.

"Who taught you to be so bold?" asked the soldier.

"My father," said Isaac smartly.

"I'd like to meet him," said the soldier. "Take me to him!"

Yechezkel was frightened. "Run," he said in Yiddish. He ran down the nearest alley. Isaac ran after him. The soldier pursued fast enough to make them scurry, but not fast enough to catch them. After a few minutes he stopped in a doorway and laughed till his sides ached.

"Poor devils," he said to himself. "I shouldn't have frightened them. How could they know that I too once went to Hebrew school and wore earlocks and a long black coat. I was afraid of chains and jail and here I am, with a sword to protect myself from Turks I've never even seen."

The two boys, meanwhile, ran in terror from one alley to another.

"He'll come after us with the dogs," groaned Yechezkel. "Why do you have to talk so much!"

"There's a wagon going out of town. Jump on!" cried Isaac. He caught the back of a farmer's wagon and pulled Yechezkel up after him. In a few minutes the wagon was at the edge of town. The farmer stopped for a moment at the drawbridge that crossed the moat and then the wagon rattled across. They jumped off at the edge of a field near a small pond.

They ducked into the tall grass at the sound of a dog's bark. Isaac pulled off his outer clothing and jumped into the pond. Yechezkel followed him.

The dog grew quiet. Frogs hopped in around them and dragonflies buzzed over their heads. Then the barking began again. The boys expected to see the soldier and a huge wolfhound, but instead a shiny little black dog jumped to the edge of the pond and sat down on their clothes. Its shrill barks cut the air like a knife. Then with one snap their clothes were in the dog's mouth and it disappeared.

Yechezkel was ready to chase it, but Isaac held him back. They stayed at the edge of the pond, cold and wet, waiting for the soldier. He didn't come. They finally crept through the high grass to the farmhouse.

They startled a family of birds. A hunter mistook them for ducks and fired above their heads. Yechezkel began to cry.

The little black dog sat on the steps of the farmhouse. He held a shoe in his mouth and sat on their coats. Isaac took a step toward him and he began to bark. He took another step and the dog dropped the shoe and put his teeth around Isaac's ankle. Isaac shrieked and the peasant came to the door.

"What are you doing here?" he growled.

"Our clothes," said Yechezkel. "Your dog has them."

"Well what do you want me to do?"

"Please make him give them back. We have to go home," said Isaac.

"Go home then," said the peasant. "I didn't invite you. I don't allow swimming here and I don't allow trampling through my field."

"We weren't swimming," said Isaac.

"I see," said the peasant. "I guess you always go around in your underwear."

They argued and argued. The peasant wanted money for the clothes. He threatened to charge their parents for the corn they had knocked down in the field. The boys wept and pleaded. By the time he agreed to let them go, the sun had sunk low in the sky.

"Shabbos!" Isaac remembered. "They'll be looking for us at the synagogue."

"The bridge," said Yechezkel sadly. "When do they lift the drawbridge? What if we're left here all night?"

They struggled into their damp, crumpled clothing and ran. The dog chased after them for a while, but they didn't even look back. They twisted their way through unfamiliar roads. They stopped only to look at the wall around the town. The soldiers marching back and forth on the top were no more than tiny specks.

They came to the iron bridge just as the soldiers prepared to pull it up, closing Zamosh for the night. They ran across and didn't stop running till they were out of sight of the garrison. But even from far off they could hear the sound of the chains and the creaking of the rusty iron.

It was dusk. Isaac imagined he saw ghosts hanging on every clothesline. Evil spirits swooped out of every chimney. Every figure seemed to be a soldier and every shadow looked like a dog.

In the Jewish section of Zamosh, however, there was Sabbath peace and quiet. They passed a

Chasidic synagogue and heard singing through the open windows. A choir was singing in the German synagogue. The streets were deserted. Candles flickered in the windows of Sabbath-clean houses. The boys came closer and closer to home, eager and afraid at the same time.

Yudele Peretz and Yechezkel's father sat together in the synagogue. They prayed together and worried together. Whenever Reb Peretz stopped looking at the door, he met his friend's eyes also turning from the door. Then it opened a crack. Two heads looked in and slipped into seats at the back. Such heads! Caps on one ear, hair full of burrs and grass, dirty clothes. Reb Peretz scarcely finished saying, "Thank You for bringing him home safely," when he added, "Will I teach him a lesson!"

He glared at his dusty son, but Isaac and Yechezkel looked neither to right nor left. The prayer book seemed to have been written for them.

"The streams have lifted, O Lord," read Isaac. "But mightier than the water, is the Lord on high."

By the time they stopped panting and their faces were cool, the service was over. A few friends followed Yudele home for kiddush, as usual. Isaac followed without a word.

Rivele threw her arms around her son as soon as he came into the house. "Thank God you're here," she said.

Isaac's father made the blessing over the wine. His friends smacked their lips at the fine taste of the honey cake. He turned to offer one of his guests a glass of wine and nearly slipped on some mud on the floor. He looked down in surprise and saw muddy tracks leading to Isaac's shoes. He walked over to his son and, without a word, slapped him across the face.

"A fine Sabbath you have made for me! A beautiful Sabbath!"

That night Isaac lay awake and overheard his parents deciding what to do with him. They had not asked where he had been. He vowed not to tell them.

He heard his father's angry voice. "To come into the synagogue in such a state. It's the last bit of foolishness I can stand. . . . We will have to send him away."

"Good," said Isaac to himself. "I'll be glad to go. No one cares about me here anyway."

He could not see the worried look on his mother's face and he couldn't hear her soft voice. "How I worry for him. Children have their heartbreak and their troubles."

"Children's troubles," said Yudele with a shrug. "Would that I had their troubles."

"He ran to his room without supper," said Rivele. "I'll take him a glass of milk if he's still up."

Isaac watched her come to his bed. His stomach was growling and he yearned for the piece of cake she held in her hand. But he stubbornly bit his lips and turned his head to the wall.

THEY... NIBBLED
ON THE BLACK · BREAD.

2

Away from Home and Back Again

The new teacher lived in Shebreshin, a small
town 20 miles from Zamosh. Isaac found out that
this teacher was a Chasid, but he wasn't too sure
of what a Chasid was. There were only a few
Chasidim in Zamosh. They had their own synagogue and their own way of praying. He listened
at the door sometimes when they were singing
and dancing. He knew that they were very pious,
even though the talmudic scholars disapproved
of them.

"At least it will be interesting," he reassured
himself.

When he was on his way, however, huddled in a corner of a half-empty coach, he became too unhappy to care whether it was interesting or not. The autumn countryside was dry and windswept and gray. He pretended that he was an orphan, alone in the world. Tears came into his eyes at the thought.

"Shebreshin!" called the driver. Isaac jumped out and pulled his bag with him. He found himself in a tiny town of perhaps a few hundred people. The coach stop was deserted until a wagon clattered up the mud road.

The driver waved and called, "Hey there, are you to go to Reb Pinkhes'?"

Isaac jumped up beside him.

It did not take long to see that there wasn't much to the town. The houses were long and low with straw-thatched roofs. The streets were unpaved. Curious people came running to look at the wagon and the driver stopped to tell them all who the passenger was.

They stopped at a house no better nor worse than the others. Isaac knocked. No one came to the door. He opened the door a crack.

"A draft! I feel a draft," a woman shouted, and came running.

"I'm Isaac Leib Peretz," he said. "I've come to study with Reb Pinkhes."

"Aie! I forgot about you," she said. "My daughter is here with her new baby and the rabbi is away. Let's see. Put your things on the bed in the corner near the door. I'll get you settled in no time."

Isaac looked around at the rough furniture and the dirt floor. He stared at the rabbi's wife and noticed how red her hands were, how dirty her apron was. He suspected that he would never get settled in Shebreshin.

Reb Pinkhes did not come home till dark. Isaac was lying on his straw-filled bed. A bag of onions was at his head. A bushel of potatoes was at his feet. The straw kept making him sneeze. He jumped up eagerly when he heard the door open and felt the cold night air in the room.

Reb Pinkhes was surprised to see him. He too had forgotten. "I'll leave you some books to read in the morning," he said. "If you have questions, bring them to me."

Isaac said nothing, but his face showed his bewilderment.

"Look, boy, I can't study for you any more than I can eat for you," said Reb Pinkhes. "Read, think, and wonder. . . . If God wills you may some day be wise."

Isaac went back to his corner far from the fire. He was too cold to sleep. I could read as well in Zamosh, he thought. Why did they send me so far to do what I could do better at home?

For the first time he realized what a fine city Zamosh was. "It's a wonder they let the moon into Zamosh at night," he used to say when they lifted the bridge and shut the city up for the night. But in Shebreshin, he even missed the walls of Zamosh, just as he missed his bed and his worktable, the polished wooden furniture in his living room and the pictures on the walls. Most of all, he longed for his mother's worried face and his father's stern eyes, his sister's teasing, and his brother's quarrels. In one day, he forgot Reb Berishel's scolding and shouting and remembered only the good times when Berishel put his angry voice aside and told fascinating tales from the Talmud and the Midrash. He forgave them all for hurting his feelings. He would gladly have walked the 20 miles home to be with them.

Isaac spent most of his day at the synagogue, reading the books Reb Pinkhes gave him. He

often forgot his questions before he had a chance
to ask them. When he wasn't studying, he
wandered through the small town listening to the
gossip in the street. He watched the children at
play and befriended a poor orphan boy to whom
he gave part of his lunch every day.

In the evenings, he burned candle after candle
while he wrote little stories and poems. He made
a friend of his notebook. He told it all his secrets
and dreams.

"There he sits," said Reb Pinkhes' wife to her
friends who came to sip tea with her. "He bites
his fingernails and grinds his shoes into the floor.
He'll make a hole under his bench some day. I
would give something to know what he writes in
that book. You can't ask him and get a civil
answer."

One evening, when Isaac came home from the
synagogue, he was amazed to hear roars and
shrieks of laughter from Reb Pinkhes' house. The
rabbi's wife and one of her friends were making
so much noise they didn't hear him open the
door.

"Listen to this," the friend said. " 'They locked

the prince in a tower with only one small window.'
He must fancy himself a prince."

"For this trash, he burns more than 20 candles
a week. Oh how I pity his parents! How did they
get such a son? He lives in a dream, like a sleep-
walker. This very morning he walked into a pail
of milk. Did you ever hear of such a thing? So
tell me more about the prince. It's the funniest
story I ever heard."

"Give the book to me," said Isaac angrily.

"Oooh," said the visitor. "Look at the eyes on
him, the burning eyes of a prince."

"By what right do you touch my book?" Isaac
shouted.

"Not so loud, young man," said the rabbi's wife.
"I'm responsible for you. I should know why you
spend so many hours wasting candles and ruining
your eyes."

"Give me my book."

"I want Reb Pinkhes to see it," she said.
"Perhaps he will send it home to your father so
that he'll know how you spend your time."

Isaac tried to pull the book out of her hand,
but he couldn't.

"Now go to the table after you've washed, and
I'll give you a nice bowl of hot cabbage soup."

"Keep your cabbage soup and give me the book."

The more furious Isaac became, the more the women laughed. With their laughter ringing in his ears he ran to his bed and, hardly knowing what he did, he threw down the bag of onions. He toppled over the bushel of potatoes. He kicked over a can of dried beans. The women tried to catch him and hold him but he was too strong and quick for them.

"A wild animal," the guest, out of breath, gasped.

"God save us from geniuses," said Reb Pinkhes' wife.

Isaac refused to pick up the vegetables until his book was returned. Since the women did not have the strength to clean up the mess, they gave the book back to him. The news of his tantrum, however, traveled throughout Shebreshin by the time he was done.

"We'll have to lock him up just like the prince in his story. I'll keep him in till the wildness dries out of him." She hid his shoes and his coat and she gave him only one candle a day, to be sure he did no more than his lessons.

The house was actually no worse than the synagogue, but Isaac could not bear to be locked up. A little before noon he remembered someone was waiting for him at the synagogue. He waited until his teacher's wife was busy at the butter churn and quietly lifted the window over his bed. He took the two slices of dark bread, the strip of dry herring and onion that she had given him for lunch and slipped out of the window. He shivered, without a jacket or shoes, but raced to the synagogue and crept into the wooden shed where the firewood was kept. He peeked throu the cracks till he saw a small boy in ragged cothes come toward him.

"Here friend," he called through a crack in the door. "I'm waiting for you."

They sat together in the freezing shed and nibbled on the black bread. The little orphan was barefoot and Isaac wore only stockings.

"What would you have done if I hadn't come," Isaac asked.

The little boy shrugged his shoulders. "I'd be hungry," he said.

The snow was falling when Isaac ran back to Reb Pinkhes' house. He lifted the window and wiggled back in.

"Isaac?" called Reb Pinkhes' wife. "Come here a minute. Help me!"

He came to help her move the churn.

"How many times must I speak to you. I called you five times."

"I didn't hear," he said innocently.

"You must be deaf," she said.

When he finished helping her, she looked at him curiously. "How cold you look. I hope you're not getting sick. Bring your book here to the fire. Your teeth are chattering."

The fire was hot enough to cook the supper, but it did not warm Isaac. His teeth continued to chatter. His head grew hotter and hotter. The straw mattress looked as inviting as his feather bed in Zamosh. When he stood up to go to it, however, it seemed far away. His knees seemed to be made of water. He held onto the chairs and tables he passed.

When he came to his bed, he fell into it. He couldn't move.

He dreamed that he was running through fire and drowning in icy pools. Reb Pinkhes' wife brought him herb tea and chicken soup. There were no doctors in the town. No one even knew the name of his sickness. The hungry orphan boy sat in the synagogue and waited day after day, but Isaac didn't come.

In Zamosh, meanwhile, Rivele Peretz was worrying. She didn't know that her son was sick, but each day looked for mail. No mail came. Reb Pinkhes was too busy to write. His wife didn't know how.

Rivele gave her husband no peace. "My heart tells me something is wrong. We must go to Shebreshin." Yudele tried to convince his wife that Reb Pinkhes would write if anything were wrong.

Rivele wouldn't listen. She hired a sleigh and a good horse. She wrapped herself in blankets and found a driver to take her to Shebreshin.

Days had passed since Isaac had eaten. He had grown thin and pale and lay for hours without opening his eyes. When he first heard his mother's voice he was so certain that he was dreaming that he didn't even bother to look to see if she were real.

The cool hand on his forehead was real, however. He put his head in her lap as he used to when he was very little and tears dripped down his cheeks for all the lonely days and nights. "Get well," she begged. "I'll take you home with me."

The same rickety wagon that brought Isaac from the coach brought them back to meet it. Rivele Peretz could not stop staring at her son with his huge black eyes in a thin hollow-cheeked face. She kept shaking her head and saying to herself, "My heart told me."

Isaac meanwhile remembered what Reb Pinkhes had taught him. He liked the teacher better and better as the miles separated them from each other. He thought of the Chasidim and admired their great faith in God and their belief that everyone could speak to Him in his own way— with a prayer, a song, with studying a difficult part of the Torah, or best of all, with a good deed. He remembered the stories and fables he had overheard in the house of study. Isaac knew that he would never forget the lessons of Shebreshin. Someday he might teach, and tell his students, "I cannot study for you. Come to me with your doubts and questions. Bring me the hard nuts you cannot crack. Read, think, and wonder. Someday you may be wise."

When he came home, Isaac's father decided that he could continue to study by himself in the synagogue. He had already taught himself much more than he would have learned in any of the classes in Zamosh. "But you must behave," his father warned. "If not, we will have to make other plans."

The first few weeks after Isaac's homecoming were wonderfully peaceful. Isaac's impulsive nature, however, had not changed. It was only waiting for an opportunity. The opportunity was not long in coming.

It was a bitter night in March. The wind whistled through the city. Isaac could not fall asleep.

At the other end of the town, close to the officers' barracks, a small fire had started from a cigarette a soldier had thrown away. It worked its way to a heap of straw in the barn. From the barn, it traveled to the piles of rubble near the walls of the town. The wind carried it to a wooden house. In a few minutes, people were screaming and jumping out of bed. A few tried throwing water on the fire, but most of them grabbed whatever they could carry and ran. The wind was faster than the people. It swept the fire right to the square, to the very edge of the tower clock.

It was quiet in the Peretz household. Isaac was the only one awake. His room was cold. His blankets were pulled right up to his nose. He saw the pink haze outdoors and thought the sun was coming up. But it was a strange sky and he finally grew so curious that he jumped out of his warm bed to see where the brightness came from. Out the window he could see the billows of smoke drifting from the square.

Isaac threw on his clothes and woke his parents. He ran out into the hall and screamed, "Fire!" By the time his parents were up and looking for him, he was gone.

Isaac ran through the dark, smoky streets. The closer he came to the square, the more people he saw. Some had pillowcases full of clothes and dishes. Others carried pieces of furniture, bedding, and pictures. Shopkeepers dragged merchandise from their stores. Hundreds of people watched the flames, hopelessly, without trying to stop them. There were no fire engines and no firemen in Zamosh.

The flames licked at the tower. Isaac watched and wept. Only a short while ago he had lain on his bed in Shebreshin and remembered the carved cupids and the bunches of grapes and leaves that decorated the tower. The gilt handles on the clock had pleased him as if they were his own property. Now it might fall and disappear forever. A thought came to his mind. The synagogue was not far. What had happened to it? He pushed through the crowds and raced toward the old wooden synagogue. Strangers tried to stop him, but he slipped away each time and ran closer to the edge of the fire. It was so smoky that he could hardly make out the building. He pushed the door open. No flames. He saw only smoke and dust. He held onto the wall so that he would not fall over any benches; he climbed up to the platform that led to the ark and finally pulled open the doors. He pulled out two of the heavy scrolls, put the silver crown on top of them and hurried out as he had come in.

The Torahs were heavy, but he was determined to bring them to his home where they would be safe. His house was made of brick. Its roof was slate. The street was paved around it.

No one was at home. His father had gone to look for him. His mother had taken the other children to the farthest wall.

Yudele, furious and terrified at once, ran looking for his son. Everyone he met was sure that they had just seen him. One man said he tried to stop him from going too close to the fire, but that he had stubbornly run right into the flames.

Meanwhile the wind died down. A snow mixed with freezing rain began to fall. The snow hit the flames with a sputtering sound. It saved the tower. The wooden frames were burned. The rope of the bell was a mass of cinders, but the tower stood firm. Little by little the rain put the fire out. People began going home or looking for homes to go to.

Rivele carried her two sleepy children back to their beds, praying as she went that Isaac had been found.

She opened the door and found her son asleep on the steps in his own hallway. His face and hands were black with soot, but he clutched the Torahs even in his sleep.

Rivele put the children in their beds and ran out to find Yudele. She found her unhappy husband, head down, hands clasped behind his back. "I can't find him," he said bitterly.

"He's found," she said. "Come home."

"All right?"

"God be thanked!" she said.

Relief turned quickly to anger. "What is wrong with him?" shouted Yudele. "How can a boy run off in time of danger and worry us to death? Has he no understanding?"

Rivele did not answer him. She just held his elbow and hurried him home.

Yudele opened the door and gasped. His son was still in the hallway, where he had sat down, exhausted. His cheek rested on the velvet cover of the Torah. Isaac opened his eyes and, half asleep, asked, "Did the synagogue burn?"

His father shook his head.

"Did the tower fall?"

"It stands," said Yudele.

"I was so afraid," said Isaac.

"Don't be afraid," said his father, gently. "God is with you. Come to bed!"

3

Trouble in Zamosh—1863

Most of Isaac's days were spent reading and studying, either in his attic room or in the synagogue. A few times a week, Reb Yossel came to help him. The teacher was a quiet, lonely old man who sat drumming his fingers on the table while they discussed the words of the prophets or some difficult passages in Maimonides.

One afternoon, the teacher kept looking up at two pictures hanging over the fireplace. One was of the Emperor Napoleon, the other of the Empress Eugenie. Yudele had brought them home one time as a souvenir of his travels. The teacher stared and stared and finally pulled himself out of his chair and yanked the pictures off the wall.

Isaac watched in amazement. "What are you doing?" he asked, afraid that the old man was out of his mind.

"They've brought us nothing but trouble," said the old teacher. "I can't stand the sight of them."

"My father said that we should be grateful to Napoleon," said Isaac. "He was a great man."

"Not this one," said the teacher. "It was the first Napoleon . . . but even he . . . Isaac, you don't understand the connection between your beloved Napoleon and the Russian soldiers who have moved in on us like parasites, getting their living from us."

Reb Yossel was deeply disturbed. That very morning new laws had been announced by the Russian government. All Poles in public office were to be replaced by Russians. No land in Poland could be sold, except to Russians.

"What has this to do with Napoleon?" asked Isaac.

Reb Yossel explained it to him from the beginning. Napoleon was the most important man in Europe when Yossel had been Isaac's age. As emperor, he brought new laws and new freedom to millions. But he also brought about long and terrible wars. The Polish people fought with the French against the Russians. At the end of the fighting Russia was in control of Poland, and it became a peaceful land, without soldiers and without supervision. Fifty years later, however, the peaceful control was over.

The first Napoleon had been dead for more than 40 years. His nephew, Napoleon III, was the emperor of France. Napoleon III encouraged Poland to rebel against its Russian master. He offered only encouragement. The rebellion broke out in Warsaw. Polish soldiers expected their friends in France to come and help them, but no help came. The Russian soldiers marched into Poland and the fighting was over in a few days.

"What did you think when the Russians marched into Zamosh?" the boy asked Reb Yossel. "There was excitement with the horses, soldiers, and music. But, Isaac, it was the end of our freedom!"

Isaac blushed because his teacher had guessed his own feelings.

"I will tell you a secret," whispered Reb Yossel. "I helped the Polish soldiers. Do you remember the clothes you children collected for the poor? Do you remember the potatoes and turnips and beans that we gathered? I drove an old wagon. Guns were hidden beneath the boards. They were covered with sacks of beans and potatoes, hidden under old clothes. I alone delivered them to the Polish soldiers as a gift from the Jews of Zamosh."

"Why didn't anyone help you?" asked Isaac.

"Why should a young man risk his life?" asked Reb Yossel. "Better an old man who has had his share of time in this world."

"What can happen now?" Isaac asked.

"I don't know," said his teacher. "When freedom is gone, anything is possible. I'm afraid for the future."

Reb Yossel's words were still ringing in Isaac's ears a few days later as the boy was walking home from his mother's shop in the square. The streets were empty. It was close to suppertime.

Isaac heard soldiers from far off. He walked faster and faster and stayed close to the walls of the houses, hoping to lose himself in the shadows. He was ashamed of being afraid, but Reb Yossel's fear had made him uneasy.

He could feel his heart pounding when a wagon stopped in front of him.

"Hey there, young man," called a soldier in Russian.

Isaac stopped and looked up at them.

"Tell us where we can get a good supper!" one commanded.

Isaac didn't understand. One soldier made the motions for eating. Another clucked like a chicken. A third lifted an imaginary glass to his lips. "Where's Bayleh?" a fourth asked.

Finally Isaac understood. He began to explain where they should go, but they didn't understand his Yiddish. They insisted that he climb into their wagon and show them the way. They sang as they rode. Little by little Isaac's heart stopped pounding.

Bayleh knew Isaac well. She didn't seem surprised to see the soldiers. She greeted them in Russian, took their coats, and told them to make themselves at home. "Wait at the door for me," she whispered to Isaac.

The soldiers settled down in the dining room and Bayleh hurried to the door, where Isaac waited curiously. "A small favor," she begged. "I'm all out of onions. Run home like a good boy and bring me a small sack."

Rivele was not yet home. He took some onions

and hurried back to Bayleh's thinking how foolish it was to be so fearful. He blamed Reb Yossel. Old people worry too much, he decided. They always expect the worst to happen.

Bayleh gave Isaac a hot roll right out of the oven and thanked him for hurrying back so quickly. When he came out into the cold again, he realized how tired he was from running back and forth. The wagon was right in front of the house. He crept onto the board underneath to rest a moment. He squeezed himself between the boxes that were stored there and munched the roll slowly, enjoying every bite.

Suddenly he saw Bayleh's front door open very slowly. Two of the soldiers slipped out, careful not to make any noise. Their coats and hats were in the house but they jumped on the wagon, took up the reins and were off. Isaac held tightly to the board beneath him, watching to see where he was going. He was too surprised to be frightened.

They went back to the square, passed the town clock, passed the courthouse and down the road that led to the officers' quarters and down a narrow lane that led to a deserted corner of the wall not far from the road to the river. The wagon stopped. The men jumped off. Isaac hid behind a bag of oats, thankful for once that he was small. A lantern flickered right in front of his nose. One of the soldiers lifted out a box, opened it, and pulled out two black coats and hats like those worn by the orthodox Jews of Zamosh. They put them on over their uniforms and jumped back into the wagon. They turned the horse around and went back to the garrison.

The wagon stopped at the sentry post. "Who goes?" called down a soldier, ready to shoot if he didn't hear the proper answer.

The soldiers in the wagon called out to him and he gave them permission to go on. The wagon stopped in a shadow. One soldier jumped down and dragged an empty sack behind him. The other had a heavy tool on his shoulder. The soldiers climbed the wall to where the sentry walked back and forth. Isaac heard a thud and a smothered cry. The boy could not see, but felt that they had hit the sentry and were putting him into the sack. He lay in his corner, terrified, with his hand over his mouth so that he shouldn't accidentally make a sound. "Why," he asked himself. "Why would Russian soldiers attack the sentry?"

The soldiers left their sack on the wall and

climbed to the office beneath the sentry's post. They had his key and opened the door. In a few minutes they were back in the wagon carrying a heavy safe, about two and a half feet square. They tried to push it under the wagon, but it wouldn't fit. They put it on top and covered it with a horse blanket.

A few minutes later they were back in the alley near the wall. The men cracked the safe with the same instrument they had used on the sentry's head. The money was stuffed into a sack they had ready and the clothes thrown down with the broken safe. In a few minutes they were back at Bayleh's. The soldiers slipped in just as they had slipped out.

Isaac held his breath. He didn't dare to move. But when the door stayed shut, he wriggled out and ran as fast as his legs could carry him. He had no idea of how long it had taken. Was it an hour? It felt to him like a year.

"Here he is," said his father angrily, as Isaac opened the door. "Why isn't it ever possible for this boy to come home on time?"

"Why do you run like that?" asked his mother. "You were so sick only a few months ago. Do you want to get sick again? Why can't you walk like a human being? It can ruin a heart, to race around like that."

"I saw a terrible thing," said Isaac, as he gasped for breath.

Yudele shook his head impatiently. "Children's terrors!"

Isaac sat down at the table and tried to tell his story. "I was coming home from the store," he said, "and some soldiers asked the way to Bayleh's; so I got into their wagon to show them the way."

"How many times have I begged you to have nothing to do with the soldiers? You are never to ride with them, never," said his mother.

"I didn't want to go," said Isaac. "But when a soldier says come, you come."

"Don't worry so much," said Yudele. "The soldiers are people too. They won't eat him up."

The discussion was over. Isaac muttered to himself, "They don't understand me and they don't believe me. How can I tell them anything?"

The news traveled rapidly through the town. According to the Polish paper, some Jews had nearly killed a Russian soldier and then broken into the officers' headquarters to steal a safe and the payroll for the soldiers in Zamosh.

Russian officers searched Jewish houses, questioned everyone, everywhere. A hat was found on the wall and carried all over town in search for a head to fit it. The general himself came to the courthouse to check the records of Jewish thieves. He couldn't believe the record. There had been only one case of Jewish thievery in Zamosh in a year and that thief was in the hospital with a broken leg.

Three suspects were thrown into jail. One was Bayleh's husband. Four officers swore that they were at his house at the time of the crime and he was not at home. Another was a tailor, who had been making new uniforms for these very officers and had not ever been paid for his work. The third was a young student, just married. Everyone was sure of their innocence, but they sat in jail and there was no word from them.

Reb Yossel suggested that all the Jews of Zamosh should march to the courthouse together to protest.

"They can't put us all in jail," agreed Yudele. "I will tell the rabbis to announce it in all the synagogues. We must do something to show that they have innocent men in jail."

At one o'clock on a Friday, the square was

packed with people. Everyone waited for the magistrate and a representative of the army to appear.

Finally the doors opened and two men came out to the top of the steps. One was the magistrate, in flowing robes. The other was an officer. Isaac took one look and gasped so loudly that his father and Reb Yossel turned to look at him. It was one of the officers in the wagon. Isaac was sure that he was one of the two men who dressed in long black coats and came to steal from their own treasury.

Everyone was quiet while the trembling rabbi spoke. An interpreter translated his Yiddish into Russian so that the magistrate and the soldiers could understand.

When the rabbi finished speaking, the magistrate came forward. "It's too late to say that they are innocent," he said. "They confessed this morning."

"Impossible," cried Bayleh, and the crowd joined her.

"We cannot believe it," said the rabbi bravely.

"You may hear it from the men themselves," said the soldier. "Come up here!"

Bayleh, the tailor's wife, and the student's wife

tried to follow the rabbi, but the soldiers held them back.

The sight of the three men brought tears to the rabbi's eyes. Bayleh's husband, a small, shy man, seemed to have become still smaller.

"Yes," he said to the rabbi. "Everything they say is true. I climbed the wall and stole the money and left a fine hat I never owned behind me to prove it."

The tailor kept his hands behind his back. "Why should I work from dawn to dusk for a few pennies, when in a moment I can steal a fortune that might last a lifetime?"

The student's eyes were bright and feverish. "You thought I was poor?" he said to the rabbi. "My wife and I live under my father's roof so that we shouldn't starve. But I'm really a great thief. I've stolen from every household in Zamosh."

When the rabbi came out, people crowded around him so that he couldn't move. He didn't say a word. Tears were streaming down his cheeks. The crowd made such a noise that it took a while before they heard the magistrate speak again. He was announcing a new proclamation. There would be military law in Zamosh until the money was returned.

"What is military law?" asked Isaac.

He soon found out. There could be no meetings, not even in the synagogue. No more than two people were permitted to walk in the street together. No one was permitted out after dark. No letters could be sent out of the town and all roads were patrolled.

The Russian soldier spoke when the magistrate was done. He sounded gentle, almost as if he were sorry to see people unhappy. "Thieves must be punished," he said, "for the protection of the city." He begged that anyone with information come straight to see him.

The crowd could not understand a word, since he spoke in Russian. They knew, however, from their rabbi's face that the men had been tortured so that they would confess to crimes they had not committed.

Cossacks on horseback drove the crowd of frightened people to their homes.

Isaac took Reb Yossel's arm and said, "Please come home with us. I must tell you something. It can't wait any longer."

At home, Isaac shut the door carefully. Rivele made tea in the kitchen and Reb Yossel and Yudele sat around the table with worried faces.

Isaac's voice broke the silence. "I know who stole the money. I saw the whole thing."

"What are you talking about?" said Yudele. "This is no time for fantasy. The whole town is in danger."

"Believe me," begged Isaac. "I'm telling the truth. Just listen to me!"

"Tell then," said Reb Yossel. "I'll believe you."

Isaac told the men his whole story. They knew from his earnestness that he told the truth.

"We must let the world know," said Yudele, when Isaac had finished. "But how?"

"I could creep under a wagon and carry a message," said Isaac.

"I won't let you," said Rivele.

"We're not sending him," said Reb Yossel.

"Uncle Altberg could send letters to Paris or to Warsaw. We could write directly to Rothschild or to Montefiore," said Isaac.

"They've stopped the mail, child," said Reb Yossel. "But let's persuade him to write the letters. I'll deliver them myself."

"What do you mean?" asked Yudele.

"I can take the same road I took last year when I went to the soldiers in the forest. If I can get to the next town, I'll be safe. It's only five miles."

"How will you walk five miles through the fields in the dark?" asked Rivele.

"And how will you get across the water?" asked Isaac. "They'll never let the bridge down."

"There are other ways," said Reb Yossel. "There's a narrow footpath across the water, hidden by rushes and weeds. I remember it from my childhood."

"But so far to walk," said Rivele again.

"I can't walk five miles," said Reb Yossel. "I will just walk ten yards, then rest, and go another ten yards. If God gives me the strength, I will get to my destination."

There seemed to be no other way. Isaac told his story again. This time Reb Yossel wrote his words down. There was a description of the officers, the place where the safe was left, the time the soldiers arrived at Baylch's and the time Isaac came home. They agreed that no one must ever know where the information came from and how it was taken out of Zamosh.

Reb Yossel tucked the slip of paper into the lining of his coat and left for Moshe Altberg's house.

"How can I write such a letter?" asked Altberg. "You won't tell me where your information comes from. You won't tell me what you plan to do with it. I have a wife and children. I can get into terrible trouble."

Reb Yossel would not give up. "If you are afraid to write in your own hand, tell me what to say and I will write."

Stubborn Reb Yossel had his way. Moshe Altberg dictated a Yiddish letter to the Jewish community of Warsaw, a Polish letter to the Polish officials who had been driven out of their posts, and a Russian letter to the army headquarters.

Late the next afternoon Reb Yossel and Yudele Peretz left with a wagon of lumber. No one stopped them till they came to the drawbridge, where two armed soldiers blocked their path.

"Where do you think you're going?" they asked.

"To Zhanov, with some lumber for the count," said Yudele.

"Turn yourselves around and go back where you came from."

"He expects me," said Yudele.

"Too bad," said the guard. "You'd better hurry. You'll be arrested if you're caught out after dark."

Yudele turned the horses around. When they

passed the lane to the fields, Reb Yossel slipped off the wagon.

Days passed like years. Rivele prayed. Isaac nervously scratched holes in his desk with a quill. Yudele waited for a hopeful word. Bayleh went to the jail every day begging for permission to see her husband, but she was turned away. There was a rumor that the men were dead.

On Friday, a tear-stained Bayleh blessed the Sabbath candles and prayed for her husband. "Don't forsake us, dear God," she begged. "Why do the innocent suffer? What sin have we committed?"

As she spoke, the door opened a crack, so slowly that no one heard until a familiar voice said, "A good Sabbath to you!" Bayleh shivered as if she had heard a ghost. But her daughter screamed, "He's home!"

Bayleh's husband was dirty and weary. His fingernails were black and his arms were bruised, but he was alive in his own house. That night, the tailor went to his family and the student to his wife. There were no apologies or explanations.

The next morning there were no soldiers in front of the synagogue, and no Cossacks patrolling the streets. The drawbridge opened and closed as usual. It was as if the last weeks had been a bad dream. The Peretz family, however, could not relax without word from Reb Yossel.

Bayleh's husband went back to study at the synagogue, the tailor to his shop, and the student to his books. One afternoon Bayleh stopped to visit Rivele. There was a knock at the door and Reb Yossel came in.

Everyone ran to embrace him. Isaac hugged him. Rivele ran for the cheesecake he loved. Yudele brought wine to the table. Isaac did not let go of his hand.

Bayleh watched in amazement. "Where are you coming from, Reb Yossel? I bet the king of England, himself, doesn't get such a welcome."

"Where have I been?" said Reb Yossel, as if he were asking himself. "I've been visiting my brothers."

"Brothers?" said Bayleh. "I thought you were the only one in your family."

"God forbid," said Reb Yossel. "I have brothers in Warsaw, in Lemberg, in Cracow."

"Did they welcome you?" asked Rivele softly.

"They behaved as brothers," said Reb Yossel.

"How did you get away?" asked Bayleh, who

was mystified by the conversation. "The town was shut up like a grave."

"I left in a good time," said Reb Yossel innocently.

"I could swear I saw you standing next to the boy, the terrible day of the proclamation. I could swear it."

"A terrible day," said Rivele. "Who could be sure of what they saw or didn't see that day."

"Then you missed it all," said Bayleh to Reb Yossel. "And if you didn't see it all with your own eyes, you'll never appreciate the miracle."

"What miracle?" asked Reb Yossel.

"The miracle of our deliverance," said Bayleh. "The town was shut off from the world. A grave injustice was done, but no one knew how or why. There were no dispatches, no visitors, only Cossacks frightening us to death every minute of the day. Suddenly help came. From where? God knows . . . I feel that my prayers were answered. Perhaps the prophet Elijah, himself, came to help us."

Bayleh picked up the sewing she carried with her wherever she went. "I have people at home to feed," she said. "Good day, friends, may we see each other only in times of joy."

When she left them, Reb Yossel put his hand on Isaac's shoulder and said, "We must never forget that there is work that even old men and young boys can do. . . . Anything is possible. . . . Even the prophet Elijah can come in modern times. Yes, Isaac," he added softly, "anything is possible—as long as men are brothers."

STUDYING...

4

Three Girls and One Boy

Three sisters lived in the apartment beneath the Peretz family. The oldest was Isaac's age. She was a shy, serious girl with soft brown eyes and smooth pink cheeks. The middle sister was as bold as her older sister was shy. She would catch Isaac in the hallway, put her hands over his eyes, and say, "Guess who?" One day she skipped down the steps, threw her arms around him, and kissed him.

Isaac dropped the books he was carrying and stood in the hallway, blushing and confused.

"Now you must come and tell my sisters. They said I would never do it. But why should I be afraid to kiss you?" chattered Gittel. "You have such nice black eyes. You know what I think? I think my sister Hannah wants you for herself, but she's too shy for you. I'm much livelier. Come on! Stop blushing and tell them how bold I am."

Isaac pulled his hand out of Gittel's. "No," he pleaded. "I can't. I can't possibly."

"I'll tell them you're afraid of us," she said. "I'll say that you think we're three horrible witches out to catch you."

"No, no," said Isaac. "I like you all. I like all of you very much."

"But you're afraid of us, I can see it in your face."

Isaac was halfway up the steps and he turned back to say, "I'm afraid that you are laughing at me."

"Hannah doesn't laugh," said Gittel. "She adores you. Sick little Malkah dreams of you. Only I laugh, and I don't mean harm. I just want to love somebody."

"Why me?" asked Isaac.

"You're the only one I know," said Gittel, and quickly blew him a kiss as he turned on the next landing.

Gittel was right. She did frighten him. Hannah was his favorite, but he didn't have the courage to speak to her and could only stare with his tongue stuck to the roof of his mouth. They had played together when they were little. Once they had even had a mock wedding. She was the bride, and he the groom. They threw pebbles and sand at each other instead of rice. Isaac threw a stone that hit Hannah's eye. She wore a patch all summer. Remembering made Isaac miserable.

One morning when Isaac was alone in the house Hannah knocked on the door. "Malkah can't catch her breath," she said. "I'm frightened. Would you stay with her while I get my mother?"

Isaac went down. The rooms were exactly like his own, but looked different. There was a glass bookcase of foreign books that he admired. Hannah's father was an educated man. Isaac always felt that her family was more modern than his.

Isaac sat down beside the frail little girl. Her face was the color of wax and her eyes burned like coals in her head. The clock ticked noisily as if it was the heart of the house, beating away.

"Isaac, listen, I want to tell you a secret," whispered Malkah. "My soul will soon fly out of me."

"No," said Isaac. "Don't say such a thing."

"It doesn't matter," she said. "I'm tired of lying

in bed. It must be marvelous to fly. Once you told me that birds were really souls, flying to heaven. Whenever a sparrow sits on my window sill, I remember what you told me and I'm glad that I have a soul that can fly."

Isaac shook his head and Malkah added, still whispering, "I love my father and my mother and my two dear sisters. I love my brother who is married and far away. But I love you more than all the others. Kiss my forehead and say good-by to me."

Isaac bent down timidly and kissed her forehead.

"Now say good-by," she whispered.

He shook his head dumbly.

Hannah, her mother, and the doctor came a few minutes later. Isaac went back upstairs. He sat at the desk near his window and watched the people come in and out of the house downstairs. He saw Gittel race down the street and the druggist rush in with a package. One doctor left and another one came.

All the rushing did not help. Malkah said good-by to her family that very night.

The next time that Isaac visited the girls downstairs, it was to a sad household. The mirrors were covered. Malkah's bed was smooth and empty. Hannah's eyes were red from weeping and there was no merriment in Gittel's face. He sat with his mother, wondering what to say that would comfort them.

Gittel came to the rescue. "Malkah said to tell you that her soul was flying into a sparrow. Poor little thing, we didn't understand what she was saying."

Isaac spoke softly so that the grownups wouldn't hear. "She was remembering a story I told her a long time ago. She was no more than four or five. I couldn't have been more than eight or nine myself. It was just after my grandfather died. Your mother was in my house with Malkah. Suddenly she looked into my eyes and asked, 'What is a soul?' I looked out the window and saw a little bird flying to heaven and said, 'My grandfather's soul will fly right to heaven.' I pointed to the bird and said, 'There goes a soul.' She believed me."

"But that's silly," said Gittel.

"I know," said Isaac. "The children at Reb Berishel's once heard what I thought and couldn't stop laughing. But when I asked them what a soul was, not one knew. I decided to find out for myself."

"What did you learn?" asked Gittel curiously.

"Reb Berishel told us that there is a great collection of souls in heaven. He said that before a Jewish child is born, an angel brings its soul down to it. He said that the souls never want to come down to this troublesome world, but they must, and they must stay until the person dies."

Gittel listened thoughtfully and then shook her head, as if she could not believe what he told her. "Who else did you ask?" she said.

"Once I met a stranger in my mother's shop. His beard was cut short and he wore his clothes in the German fashion. He was looking over the rolls of cloth. I imagined that it must be so in heaven too: the souls stretched out on shelves, and the angel choosing this one or that. I told the stranger my thoughts and even a little of what Reb Berishel had explained at school."

"He must have thought you were crazy," said Gittel.

"Worse than that," said Isaac. "He became so angry he pounded his fist on the counter and said, 'Remember *all* people have souls! All have the same eyes, the same hands, and the same feet. All laugh for joy and weep when they're sad. God is the father of all. The earth belongs to all. We are all equal children with souls of equal value.' "

"Why then," asked Hannah softly, "does every country think it is the best and that God loves its people best of all? Poles think they are better than the Russians. Russians feel better than the French."

"I asked the same questions," said Isaac. "Do you know what he said? He promised me that a better time would come. He believed that someday all people will know one God and one law. Our prophets will be everyone's prophets. There'll be no war and no hatred and Torah will come out of Jerusalem."

"How fine it sounds," said Hannah. "If it could only be."

"But Reb Yossel didn't agree. He says that we aren't like other people. He said the child the father loves the most is the one he spanks the hardest. If God punishes, it is also so the best of his children should learn and improve."

"But what has that to do with a soul?" asked Hannah.

"Reb Yossel says that there are all kinds of

souls, that they are not equal. There are fat ugly ones and beautiful sparkling ones. There are ordinary grayish and brownish ones. They go back and forth from heaven to earth just as Reb Berishel said. The trouble the soul knows on earth sends it back to heaven purer and finer than when it came."

"You make it sound as if a soul was like the coarse grain the farmers bring to my father's mill. The first grinding makes the grain whiter and finer. The more it's ground, the better it becomes. . . . The finest souls must be like the finest flour for the Sabbath bread. . . . But I don't know if I believe you, either," said Gittel, with a shake of her head. "I'll be wondering all my life."

Gittel's mother called her and she left Isaac and Hannah alone for a moment.

"Do you know, then, what a soul *is?*" Hannah asked.

Isaac shook his head and looked into her warm brown eyes. "You are my soul," he said.

"What are you whispering?" Hannah's mother asked crossly.

"We were talking about Malkah," said Hannah, with a flushed face and moist eyes.

Before Isaac went up with his mother, Hannah

asked, "Can you read Polish? My father brought some new books."

"Only a little," said Isaac. "I've been teaching myself."

"I'll help you if you want me," said Hannah.

"Thank you," said Isaac. "I'll teach you Hebrew in exchange." He left with two books under his arm. "May we see each other only in times of joy," he said, just as his mother did.

One day, Isaac pushed his chair away from his desk and bolted out of the door. He jumped down the steps two at a time and pulled the door open so quickly that Hannah, who was leaning on it, fell to her knees.

"I'm so sorry," he apologized. "That's twice I've hurt you."

Hannah rubbed her arm where she had bumped it and said, "Twice? How twice?"

"Don't you remember your eye?"

She had forgotten, but she rubbed her finger on a small scar beneath her eye. "I could have lost my eye," she said.

"God forbid," said Isaac.

"Who would have wanted me with only one eye?" she asked coyly.

"I," said Isaac.

"You would love me with only one eye?" she asked.

"Forever," he said. He smiled to make it seem that he was teasing, but his eyes were serious. When Hannah looked back at him, it was as if he were looking into a mirror.

A few months later, however, Hannah's father came home from a long journey and greeted his daughter very warmly.

"What is the news?" she asked.

"Wonderful news, daughter," he answered. "I haven't been traveling for nothing. A fine man has spoken for your hand. I've been making the necessary arrangements. We won't have an engagement until the time of mourning is past. But with God's help, it will all be for the best."

"Without telling me?" she said.

"This is a father's responsibility, not a child's," he said fondly.

A few days passed before Isaac saw Hannah. He wondered what had happened to her. He knocked at her door whenever he went out, but no one answered. Yet he was sure she was at home. He waited till he saw her mother come into the house before he came again. He brought his Hebrew book for her lesson and the Polish book for his.

"Isaac, I'm sorry," said Hannah's mother, with a smile. "I think it's time to stop the lessons with Hannah. She has other things on her mind."

"What other things?"

"What other things, indeed," said the woman. "Isaac, you're almost 15 years old and Hannah is a few months older than you. There's talk of an engagement, not tomorrow, of course, but it's bound to come. So we must stop the lessons."

"But what harm is there in her studying?" asked Isaac.

"Studying, and whispering, and holding hands, it's all one. How would you like it if your intended was so busy with another young man? He's a fine man, much older than you, with a good business."

Isaac stared, bewildered.

"Look at the long face. Hannah's almost like a sister to you. It won't be long before you too are betrothed and you'll understand. So be a good fellow and leave our books alone. If you have a minute, do me a favor and get me two pails of water. The water carrier brought enough this morning, but Hannah accidentally dropped the pail. She's distracted with excitement, poor child."

Isaac took the pails and went down the steps. "A modern man," he muttered aloud. "A modern father teaches his daughters languages and then marries them off like cattle. He can't!" he said so loudly that people turned to stare at him. "He has no right to do such a thing," he shouted as he swung his pails.

The well was in the square. A few steps led down to the deep spring-fed hole that provided most of Zamosh with its water. In the morning there was a long line waiting, but Isaac was the only one there when he came. He stopped to look down into the darkness and leaned on the sign that was propped up against the stones. The sign that said, "UNDER REPAIR" fell into the well. The stone beneath it splashed in after it. Isaac's pails slipped out of his hands in the excitement and he teetered on the slippery tile and tried to catch his balance.

A firm hand caught his shoulder. An unfamiliar voice said, "Hey there, can't you read?"

Isaac steadied himself, looked around, and saw

that the well was surrounded with signs warning that the well was under repair.

"You might have arranged yourself a watery grave," said the stranger. "It's a lucky thing I was passing by."

"Thank you," said Isaac breathlessly.

Isaac fixed the pails to lower into the well and the stranger stared. "Aren't you the Peretz boy?" he asked.

Isaac looked at a short man with a long head. He wore a peculiar old velvet jacket and smelled of snuff and tobacco. "Who are you?" he asked. "I don't know you."

"You don't know Michel, the fiddler? My feelings are hurt. But you see I know you and I know that those who don't say that you're a bit peculiar, say that you're a bit of a genius. Are you?"

Isaac didn't know what to answer.

"I've been looking for you. I want to make a bargain with you," said Michel.

"What kind of bargain?" asked Isaac curiously.

"I have a bit of Kabbalah I want translated. Don't ask me why . . . because it's not your affair. I just happen to need it and I was told that you can translate it. Can you?"

"Perhaps," said Isaac.

"Then come to see me," said Michel. "And for my part of the bargain, I will give you this." He took a small brass key out of his pocket. It was a key to his door. "I have a library of modern books, the best in Zamosh. Come and read! Make yourself at home!"

Isaac put the key in his pocket and tried to thank the stranger, but Michel didn't stop to listen.

Isaac soon set the pails of water down at Hannah's door. He knocked loudly and ran upstairs before the door was opened.

THE DRIVER WHISTLED...

5

The Runaway

Isaac went to the synagogue early every morning to pray and study. Before lunch, however, he would slip out and hurry to Michel's house. It stood alone, at the edge of town. There was an old apple tree in front of the porch and some overgrown hedges at the sides. The wooden steps were broken and the shutters hung loosely on their hinges. The rooms inside were bare and dusty and only the library was in good order. It was a house to match its owner.

Isaac began with the first book on the top shelf and went on to read around the room, book by book in whatever order he found them. He kept a dictionary at his side. The books were in Polish, French, German, and Russian. He taught himself the languages as he read.

Isaac's old friend, Yechezkel, watched him go off every day. His feelings were hurt because Isaac didn't tell him where he went or invite him to go along. One afternoon he decided to follow Isaac and see where he spent his afternoons. Yechezkel watched him go into the deserted house. He couldn't contain his curiosity and followed him.

Isaac jumped at the sound of footsteps. "What are you doing here?" he asked angrily when he discovered Yechezkel.

"What are *you* doing here?" asked Yechezkel.

"I'm educating myself," said Isaac. "I'm out in a great market place, meeting people from all over the world."

"Are you all right?" asked Yechezkel, as he pointed to his head.

"Of course I'm all right," said Isaac. "You just have no idea of how big the world is, how many things there are to learn."

"For instance?" said Yechezkel.

"For instance, this is an algebra book," said Isaac.

"What's algebra?" asked his friend.

"It's a way of counting," said Isaac.

"What do you have to count for?"

"It's not a question of what I have to count. It's important for physics, for astronomy, for understanding the universe."

"I see," said Yechezkel, but Isaac saw from his friend's face that he couldn't see at all. "What is physics?"

Isaac tried to think of something easy. "I read," he said, "that you may think your clothes keep you warm, but it's not true. You, in fact, keep your clothes warm. Do you understand?"

Yechezkel looked completely bewildered. "Never mind," said Isaac. "There are easier sciences to understand than physics. I have a biology book that tells how plants grow, how birds live and mate, how the sap in a tree goes upward."

"But what is the use of it?" asked Yechezkel. "Are you planning to grow plants or raise chickens? What are you planning?"

"Why do you study Rashi, or the prophets, or the mysteries of the Kabbalah?" asked Isaac. "What are you planning?"

"We're commanded to study Torah," said Yechezkel. "Where in the Bible does it say we must study algebra and physics?"

"We study history in the Torah, why not the history since biblical times?"

"To tell the truth," said Yechezkel, "I've never seen much point to history. Old troubles and old battles and the world stays the same."

"How can you be so foolish?" asked Isaac. "Are we shepherds today in Palestine? Are we doctors in Spain? Are we living in a miserable pale of settlement? We're citizens of Poland! We have rights! We have privileges. We're free to study what we wish."

"Really, Isaac," said Yechezkel angrily, "I think all this reading has addled your brain. You've forgotten all about the martial law and how Bayleh's husband was thrown into jail for nothing."

"It doesn't have to happen," said Isaac. "The world *can* change. People can learn and improve. They don't have to hate each other."

"Sure," said Yechezkel. "Find a Polish friend and try out your ideas. See how well they work!"

"I have a Polish friend," said Isaac sharply. "His name is Janek Polnievsky. He lives next door and sometimes helps me out with words I don't understand. He's studying to be a doctor and he too believes the world can change and improve."

"Sure," said Yechezkel sceptically. "But where does the market place come in? I hardly know what you're talking about."

"Don't you see, a library is a kind of market place; not for cabbages and turnips, but for ideas, new thought, and inventions. You don't have to like everything you see, but it's exciting to look everything over. Look at this picture," said Isaac as he opened a book. "Guess what it is."

Yechezkel couldn't guess.

"It's a carriage that goes without horses," said Isaac.

"You don't say," said Yechezkel with a grin.

"It's true," said Isaac.

"Sure," said Yechezkel. "Next you'll tell me that men are flying to the moon. I don't believe any picture I see. Come on back with me for the evening prayer."

"No," said Isaac. "I'll stay till it gets dark."

"Stay then! Get Janek to keep you company," Yechezkel said angrily as he left.

Left alone, however, Isaac was overcome by a feeling of sadness. He had so many questions and no one to ask them of.

"Why are people so unkind to each other?" he

asked himself. "Why did God invent death? What is a soul and what is sin? If God didn't create the world, where could it have come from? But what did God make the world *for?* What did he create *me* for?"

At home that night, his parents were asking themselves the same question but in a more practical way.

"Isaac has to learn a trade. He has to be able to make a living," said Yudele.

"What do others do?" asked his mother.

"Some send their sons to study to be doctors or lawyers. Others send their children to the government schools in Warsaw. Your cousin said he could come to his mill and learn about grinding. My uncle with the brewery would take him in and teach him the trade."

Rivele didn't answer. She didn't want Isaac to leave home. The big cities frightened her and she certainly didn't want her favorite son in a mill or a brewery.

Isaac listened angrily from his room upstairs. "How easily they decide for me," he said to himself. "Why don't they ask me what I want? Don't I have anything to say?"

According to Michel, there was only one solution. He insisted that Isaac must leave Zamosh and go to Vilna to study. "All your questions will be answered there," he said.

Even Hannah agreed, when he told her what Michel suggested. "Go," she said in her soft voice. "Don't stay here. Make your fortune in the city."

"Don't tell your parents," said Michel. "Just go!"

"How can I go without money?" Isaac asked.

"Who cares for money?" said Michel recklessly. "I'll pawn my gold watch for you."

"How will I get there and what will I do? Where will I live?"

Michel had an answer for every question. He knew of a coachman who would take Isaac for a small fee. He had friends who would offer food and lodging in exchange for Hebrew lessons.

"Why do you do this for me?" asked Isaac. "Why should you care what becomes of me?"

Michel put his arm around Isaac's shoulders and in a wistful voice said, "I'm getting to be an old man. I've no wife, no child. Once I too was a bright boy. I was sure I was going to set the world on fire. I've wandered like a gypsy from city to city, without success in any place. Nothing will ever be right for me, Isaac. I'm hopeless. But if I could help somebody, you for instance, it would give me a reason for having been created."

Isaac hesitated, but Michel was sure. "Go tomorrow," he said. "My friend leaves before dawn. I'll leave the money with him. Slip away while the household sleeps. Run, child, run before it's too late."

Isaac agreed.

He had to tell someone. When he met Hannah, on his way home from Michel's, he knew that she would listen. "Do I have the right to run away like this?" he asked.

"Isaac, you must," she said softly. "You have the best mind in Zamosh. It would be a sin to hide yourself here forever. I'll explain it to your mother."

Isaac was slow to go to bed that night. He sat on his little sister's bed and told her a story.

His younger brother was waiting to ask him something. "Do I understand this Maimonides correctly?" he asked. "I think it says that there is no pain, no suffering and no death. That God gives only light and the absence of light. Do I understand it properly? It's so hard to understand it."

"Don't bother your head with that," said Isaac, just as his elders had told him.

"It's your book I'm reading," protested his brother.

"It's too much for both of us," said Isaac.

"Time for bed," said their mother. She watched Isaac, while he looked around their living room intently, as if he were saying good-by to it.

"Your father will be back in a few days," she said.

"That's fine," said Isaac in a flat voice.

He shut the door of his room tightly. Then he tied his few belongings in a pillow case and tucked them under his bed. He ran his hand over his dresser. He touched his desk and his chair. His heart felt so heavy. It was as if he were already gone and already homesick. He heaved a great sigh and blew out the candle.

His eyes refused to close. A coach rattled by. A mouse scratched in the wall. The moon shone into his window, throwing more light than the candle. He wondered what would happen if the driver whistled for him before dawn and he didn't hear. He worried what his mother would say when she found him gone in the morning. Hannah had promised to explain for him. Was it a mistake to let her? She would be blamed for his going. But wasn't it her fault, more than anyone's?

Suddenly his door opened very slowly. His mother came in, in her nightgown, with a kerchief on her head. Her feet were bare. She sat down on the chair next to his bed. Tears dripped softly from her closed eyelids.

Was she saying good-by to him? Who could have told his secret? Had Hannah whispered it to Gittel? Had their mother overheard?

Rivele sat at her son's bed for a long time, without saying a word. Isaac wished that she would scold him or argue with him so that he could be angry with her. He did not know how to fight quiet tears. He opened his mouth and closed it without speaking. She didn't help him. When she got up to go, she kissed his forehead as if he were a little child and said, "God be with you."

"Good night, mother," he said. "Sleep well."

The coach came with the first crack of light in the sky. Isaac lay on his bed with his clothes on and his sack at his side. The driver whistled and he jumped down from the bed. Isaac passed his mother's door on tiptoe. He was so quiet that he could hear the sobs she tried to bury in her pillow.

Hannah waited in the hall. A coat covered her nightgown. Her braids hung like two snakes around her shoulders. "Let me kiss you good-by," she whispered.

"Don't kiss me," said Isaac. "I can't go."

Hannah rushed past him to her door without a word. "My mother," he started to say, but her door was shut before he finished.

Isaac ran to the corner to tell the driver to go on without him. The driver was angry that he had waited for nothing. "Hear that," he called to the passengers. "They all say the boy's crazy. Believe them!"

Back in his room, Isaac threw his bundle to the floor and banged his fist on his dresser. He looked into the mirror and said to his reflection, "What's wrong with you? You run away and run away and run away . . . and you're still at home."

MARRIED

6

A Wedding!

Rivele Peretz sat at the dining room table, sewing.

"If one doesn't go, one can't be sorry," said Rivele to no one in particular.

Isaac covered his notebook with his hand so that no one would see what he wrote. In dark letters he had written, "Everything has fallen to pieces for me."

Marie, the Polish maid, was polishing silverware. "You know," Rivele said to her, "the later the sun comes up, the finer the day is. . . . Everything happens for the best."

Marie shook her head, but Isaac covered his face with his hands. Could it be "for the best" that he should feel so trapped, that his friends with half his ability should go off to become doctors and lawyers while he stayed in his room, fishing for problems? "My problems," he wrote, "grow up around me like mushrooms."

"Why must I please everyone, and not myself?" he wrote. "I am I. I am here. The rest of the world may be a dream for all I know. I won't let them break me, as if I were a horse."

A few long days of waiting passed. Yudele came home. His wife greeted him warmly. She had been worrying so about Isaac and grieving for his unhappiness without being able to help him. Before she could share her fears with her husband, however, he said. "Congratulations, *mazel-tov,* Isaac's troubles are over."

Yudele told them his news. A wedding had been arranged for Isaac with the daughter of Gabriel Lichtenfeld, a well-known scholar and philosopher.

"A fine young woman," said Yudele, "and a proper dowry. A beautiful family . . . the wedding can be in the fall . . ."

Rivele stared at her son. He listened as if they were talking about someone else. "What do you say, Isaac?" she asked.

"What is there to say?" said his father. "Lichtenfeld is a famous man. It's a great honor for Isaac."
Yudele put his arm around his son's shoulders.
"May you have everything good that we wish for
you!"

Rivcle still stared at him anxiously, waiting for
a word, one way or the other.

With a shrug of despair, Isaac said, "Whatever you wish, I will do."

In the next few weeks, Isaac's moods changed
like the weather. One day he wrote, "I've given
in. I see no other way. My mother's tears have
killed me." Another day he was more optimistic.
He wrote, "Perhaps this is truly for the best. It
will be good to have Lichtenfeld for a father-in-
law. I can ask him all my questions. He'll know
what I should study and where. He'll open up a
door to the world for me."

Isaac kept his nose in a book all day and didn't
even think of his bride. He didn't know what
she looked like or what kind of girl she was.
He told himself that it made no difference. She
wasn't Hannah. He tried to forget about the
wedding day that drew closer every morning.

The thoughts he kept hidden in the daytime,
however, came to haunt him at night. He dreamed

that he came to a wedding. The bride sat in a high chair, with a veil over her face. He went up to her and lifted the veil. Sometimes she was blind. Sometimes she was terribly ugly or stupid. In one dream she stood up to come and meet him, but she was lame and couldn't walk. He would wake up with a groan and shake the bad thoughts out of his head.

A few days before the wedding, Isaac lost his patience. "They are not to cut off my bride's hair," he said. "Tell Lichtenfeld that I won't go through with the wedding if she comes to me shorn like a sheep!"

Yudele became angry. All Jewish girls had their hair cut short before they were married. Rivele, however, let Isaac have his way. Word was sent to Lichtenfeld that his daughter Sarah was not to cut her hair. Yudele scolded, "What was good enough for your mother and your grandmother is good enough for your bride." But Isaac was determined to have his way in little things, now that all the big things were given to him without any choice. On the day of his wedding, when he was supposed to fast, he came into the kitchen and tasted every piece of cake that he could find.

Isaac had dreamed of his wedding so many

times that the real day seemed to him as much a dream as the others. The wedding was at an inn in the town of Apt and the Peretz family and friends left Zamosh early in the morning. Isaac was in a large carriage, drawn by two horses. His shoes pinched his feet and the unfamiliar hat pressed down on his head. Neighbors came out to call, "*Mazel-tov!*" as they passed. Isaac's sister and brother were laughing and chatting as they rode, but he sat still and numb, feeling like a leaf carried along in a windstorm.

The faces in the inn at Apt were unfamiliar. Lichtenfeld, the scholar, looked quite ordinary in spite of his reputation. He shook Isaac's hand without interest and hardly looked into his face before he disappeared with Yudele. Isaac stayed to shake the hands of uncles, aunts, friends, and cousins. The children went to see the bride and watch the musicians.

Joshua came back quickly to report, "She's pretty, Isaac. You're lucky!"

Moshe Altberg came to say, "Good luck. You have a fine, educated girl. You'll have a good life together."

Yudele boasted to Lichtenfeld of his distinguished family of learned men, rabbis, and scholars. Lichtenfeld boasted about his relatives. "A perfect match," they all agreed. But Isaac's hands were wet and clammy. The musicians played, but he didn't hear them.

Isaac noticed a group of poor children standing at the edge of the lawn, watching, and he went to get some cookies and some coins for them so that they could share in the celebration. As soon as he came back, he was called to the wedding canopy. The musicians began to play for the bride. Everyone grew quiet, so that the rabbi could be heard.

"Blessed art Thou, O Lord, who sanctifies thy people Israel by the rite of the canopy and the sacred . . ."

A clap of thunder drowned his words. Rain came down in sheets before the rabbi could say another word. The guests in their fine clothes waited in the rain. Only Isaac ran wildly to the house, leaving his bride in the rain. Sarah began to cry and then ran after him. The rabbi, the canopy, the guests, and musicians followed them into the inn.

Yudele was furious. "Such a commotion over a bit of rain," he said. "What's the matter with the boy?"

Lichtenfeld found it all very amusing. "The bridegroom is determined to run this wedding," he said. "He leads and we must follow."

By the time everything was brought indoors, the storm was over.

The next morning, Isaac awoke in a strange room and in an unfamiliar bed. At first he imagined he was still dreaming, but little by little he remembered everything. The wedding in the rain, Lichtenfeld, the guests, the musicians, and Sarah, his bride. The worry and the waiting were over. She was neither lame nor blind, neither ugly nor old. She was just an ordinary girl. Suddenly he remembered how he had left her alone under the canopy while he ran from the rain. He blushed at the thought of it. "Why did I do it?" he asked himself. He knew why. He wanted to run away from his bride and his family. He wanted to be free to decide his own life, but all he could do was disrupt his own wedding ceremony for a few minutes.

Sarah Lichtenfeld Peretz huddled at the opposite side of the bed with a blanket pulled over her head. She wept so softly in her pillow that Isaac couldn't hear and didn't know that she wasn't asleep until he saw her shoulders shaking with sobs. He realized that she was as unhappy as he. "Don't cry," he begged. "We're caught, both of us, like two foolish fish, in the same net."

She sobbed even louder. "I'm not a fish," she said. "I'm a person with feelings."

"Please," begged Isaac, "let's talk to each other. I don't even know the sound of your voice. . . . Don't cry. We'll work it out. . . . Our parents were married the same way. . . . It won't be so bad. . . . But let's talk and not cry. I can't stand crying. . . . Let me see your face. Please."

"I have nothing to say," said Sarah, and she pressed her face, deep, deep into the pillow.

HE HAD FIVE RUBLES

7

Earning a Living

While Sarah Lichtenfeld Peretz was growing up in her scholarly father's house, she had dreamed of marrying a rich husband who could take good care of her. She longed for pretty clothes, a fine house, and servants to make her life easy. Her father, however, had married her to an eighteen-year-old boy who had only the money she brought in her dowry, who did not have a livelihood, and was a scholar without special talent for business.

Isaac had dreamed of a wife who would be a friend and a helpmate. Though it was not then the fashion to educate girls and boys in the same way, he thought girls should study just as boys did. He wanted someone who could share his interest in books and in ideas and someone who would be patient with him until he found his place in the world.

Two years after their wedding, Isaac and Sarah were still strangers. Sarah was disappointed because he could not find a good job. Isaac felt completely alone. There were too many quarrels that ended in tears and silence. "Please understand me," he begged, but Sarah would put her hands over her ears and refuse to listen.

"Aren't you a clever fellow," she would taunt. "You know everything, everything but how to earn some money."

Isaac had expected that they would live with the Lichtenfelds until they were settled. The Lichtenfelds, however, had only a small apartment in Warsaw. The parents decided that it would be better for Isaac and Sarah to live in Zamosh until they could afford a home of their own.

Isaac went to the forest with his father to see if he too could sell lumber, but there was no room for an inexperienced young man. Isaac went from town to town, looking at a mill, a wine press, though he knew nothing about milling or making wine. At home, he spent his time at the writing desk in his old familiar corner. Sarah would come up behind him and ask, "What are you scribbling? Poetry? Philosophy? Or is it something practical? How much is left of my dowry, for instance?"

One night he came home with news. "I've bought a mill," he said with excitement.

"What do you know about milling?" Sarah asked.

"I have a partner," said Isaac. "He knows the work and seems a decent man. I'll buy the equipment with the money we have left, but then there will be money earned every week. We'll find a place of our own to live in. Everything will be better."

"Where is it?" asked Sarah.

"In Apt," said Isaac.

"Another stupid little town," said Sarah angrily. "As if it hasn't been bad enough here. There is nothing to do here in Zamosh and there'll be less in Apt."

"Some women find enough to do," said Isaac angrily.

"What do you expect me to do? If I had a house, I would take care of it. If I had money, I would spend it. I wait for you all day, and then you sit and scribble till the small hours. What can you do here? Walk to the market place and look at the peasants and their cabbages?"

"You could read," said Isaac.

"Reading is for people who have nothing better to do. I want to have a good time. I don't want to stick my nose in a book."

"If the mill does well, we can try to get one close to Warsaw. I too would like to live in a big city, but it's not possible now."

Isaac and Sarah went to live in Apt. But Isaac's dream of prosperity didn't come true very quickly. His partner seemed to know his job. The farmers brought their grain. The machinery worked. But at the end of the week there was hardly any money to take home.

One autumn day, Peretz vowed that he would force his partner to explain why they couldn't make a profit. Isaac had been sick and away from the mill for a few days. Sarah had insisted that he do something about the mill. They were expecting their first child and she was even less patient than before.

Isaac found the mill shut. His partner was not

in sight. Isaac had forgotten his key. He pried open a window and climbed through.

The mill was empty. The grinding machine was gone. The flour bins had been removed. Isaac began to tremble as if he had a fever. It was like a bad dream. All he heard was his own footsteps and the wind rattling the window. Tacked on the wall was a note. It said: "Dear Peretz, You aren't cut out to be a businessman. You were bound to lose your money sooner or later. It was better for me that it should be sooner. I sold the machinery and the safe and I'm off for America. Don't bother searching for me. You won't find me. Good luck!"

"Thief!" shouted Isaac and banged his fist into the wall. No one heard but the mice and the spiders. He ran to the police, but they weren't interested in his story. He showed them the note, but they said that they knew the miller. He told them that he had worked for months without pay.

"It's not true," said Isaac. "He took every penny."

Isaac didn't even have a copy of the contract or the deed for the mill. The papers were in the safe that had been emptied and sold. Without proof of ownership, he couldn't even sell the building. The town of Apt took it. The police seemed to know exactly what to do. "Go see a lawyer," the chief of police said to Isaac. "We can't help you."

Sarah was in bed when Isaac came home. "I come with empty hands," he said bitterly. "I knew," she said. "I knew it all the time." "How could you know?" he said. "Who told you?"

"When have you tried to please me?" she asked. "Do you even think of me? You care only for your books and scribbling."

"Why are you talking riddles?" Isaac asked, bewildered. "Why did I buy the mill? Only to please you."

"You never bought me a present. I'm eighteen years old today and I've not so much as a good wish, not a flower, a stone, or a shawl. That's how much you care."

Isaac put his hands in his empty pockets and turned them inside out. Not a coin fell to the floor. "With what shall I buy?" he asked. "Everything is lost. The mill and everything in it. The dowry is used up . . . all stolen . . . gone."

Their first son was born a few weeks later and they named him Jacob. The joy over his birth was short, however. When the baby was a month old he caught a cold that turned to pneumonia. The little one's life went out like a candle.

Yechezkel met Isaac in the street one day and hardly recognized him. Two years of marriage had taken the flashing look out of his eyes. He looked old and tired.

"The trick," said Isaac, with pretended cheerfulness, "is to keep on whistling. Even if your mouth doesn't want to, you just have to whistle and pretend everything is fine."

"Have faith," said Yechezkel. "The wheel may turn. You'll see; better times will come."

The old troubles, however, were back. Isaac and Sarah had a second son and they called him Lucien, but Isaac couldn't find a job. They were forced to come back to live with his parents in Zamosh. The days went by in hunting for work. In the evenings, Isaac taught himself bookkeeping and wrote stories, poems, some in Hebrew and some in Polish, without knowing what to do with them.

Each day seemed worse than the one before.

Sarah was unhappy. The baby was always crying. Isaac made a difficult decision.

One night he slipped out of bed. He kissed his
sleeping son, took a bag with some clothes and
some of his stories. He left a note for Sarah and
his mother and left the house. He took a carriage
to the new railroad station and bought a ticket
for Warsaw.

In the morning Sarah read:

> Dear Wife,
> Forgive me for leaving you. I can't quarrel
> any longer. I am going to Warsaw to work and
> study. I will send you whatever I earn. I will
> not stay away a day longer than I must. I see
> no other way. Love from your devoted husband
> who wishes for your happiness.

Isaac came out of the Warsaw railroad station
with a pounding heart. He had five rubles in his
pocket and no idea of where to go or whom to
consult. Lichtenfeld was the only one he knew
in Warsaw, but Isaac dreaded seeing him. The
streets were crowded with people, carriages, and
wagons. Isaac stood and gawked like any small-
town boy new to the city. He stared at the shops

and the crowds, marveling that there should be so many people and not one familiar face.

He felt so much alone that he didn't even turn when someone called his name. He walked along open-mouthed till someone caught his arm and shouted, "Where do you think you're going?"

Isaac couldn't believe his eyes. "Michel," he said, "if I ever wished to see anyone it was you, this very minute."

"How long have you been here?" asked Michel.

"An hour, maybe two," said Isaac.

"You're only four years late. . . . But where are you staying? What are you planning to do?"

"I want to go to the university but I need a job and a place to sleep. I have no money."

"I won't pawn my watch for you," said Michel, "but come home with me. I have friends. We'll work something out."

Michel was as good as his word. He found two students who let Isaac use their couch in exchange for Hebrew lessons. He found a merchant who needed a bookkeeper and, most important, he arranged for an interview at the university. Isaac was accepted as a law student and a tutor in language and literature. His teaching would pay his tuition.

The room that Isaac shared with the students was always full of their friends discussing books, politics, and religion. Isaac could talk about ideas and problems that had troubled him all his life. He was surrounded by friends who liked to listen to him and argue with him.

One Saturday Isaac hiked halfway across the city to visit his father-in-law. Gabriel Lichtenfeld was reading when Isaac came in. His wife was asleep. The older man welcomed Isaac with more warmth than he expected. He said he had been waiting for him. Sarah had written.

"So the business is done for," Lichtenfeld whispered, not to awaken his wife.

Isaac shook his head and waited for a lecture.

"Why don't you study law?" Lichtenfeld said, to Isaac's surprise.

"That's what I'm studying," said Isaac.

"Good," he said. "And what about the scribbling Sarah complains about? What are you writing?"

Isaac blushed. "Stories, poems, some essays," he said.

"Send some to me," said Lichtenfeld. "Maybe they can be published." He stood up, put his arm around Isaac's shoulders and led him out to the hallway. "I'm sorry that Sarah is giving you a hard time."

"I send her every penny I earn," said Isaac.

"I'm sure of it," said Lichtenfeld, "but it's hard for my wife to understand. Go before she wakes. I'll give her your good wishes."

Isaac thanked him and left. For the first time, he realized that Lichtenfeld had his own problems. He didn't have much money, in spite of his scholarship. He was afraid of his wife. What seemed like coolness was really shyness.

That night, Isaac began to do his homework just as the others went to bed.

"Don't you ever get tired?" one of the boys asked.

"No," teased another. "He doesn't get tired. He's not human. He's a sponge that soaks everything up."

"Go to sleep, fellows," Isaac begged. "You can stay and study for four years, I have to get home. I have a wife and a son to take care of."

"Nobody can take a four-year course in a year and a half while they're teaching and tutoring and lecturing and doing bookkeeping. It's impossible!"

⌐ "I told you he wasn't human," said the other boy, as he stuffed his head into his pillow, "so don't be surprised!"

Months flew by like days, for Isaac. He had never worked so hard or been so happy. He had many friends, his classes were well attended, and his own studies seemed easy to him. When Lichtenfeld sent Isaac a copy of a magazine with one of Isaac's own poems in it, he was overcome with gratitude. He felt that he could do anything he tried. He even looked forward to returning to Zamosh with his new ability and his new confidence. He thought how fine it would be to have a law office of his own, with his own name on the door. He decided that he would keep the name they had given him at the university. His teacher had turned Isaac Leib Peretz into the Polish, Leon Perec. He could see it clearly on a shingle outside the house, Leon Perec, Advocate.

8

Leon Perec, Advocate

The sign was in the window in Zamosh but no one
came. Isaac did some bookkeeping and gave some
Hebrew lessons. After a few discouraging weeks
went by, he went to see his Uncle Altberg to ask
his advice.

Moshe Altberg pulled his beard for a few
minutes and said, "How would you like to help
me? I have too much work here. You can do the
research and I'll have more time to spend in
court."

It was more than Isaac dared hope for. He was
determined to prove that he could be completely
responsible and a real help to his uncle. One

winter day Altberg was sick and could not appear in court. Isaac impulsively decided to take his uncle's place. The client was angry until Isaac began to speak. He knew then that there was nothing to worry about. Isaac's quick wit and his remarkable memory were an immediate success.

When the court session was over, Isaac went back to the office to finish his day's work. As he worked, however, he began worrying whether his uncle might be angry with him, whether he might be offended because he didn't ask his permission.

When Moshe Altberg woke from his afternoon nap, Isaac stood at the foot of his bed and stammered, "Don't be angry, Uncle. I have to tell you what happened today."

"I thought you were a great orator," Altberg said. "A marvelous speaker who holds people spellbound with his words, logical, scientific. So what are you stuttering about?"

"What do you mean?" asked Isaac.

"I know all about it. For goodness sake, the news was all over town 15 minutes after court was out."

"You're angry," said Isaac. "I know you're angry and I'm so sorry."

"I'm not angry, foolish boy. I'm pleased. I'm

glad to have an assistant to speak for me without shaming me."

It was the beginning of Isaac's career. Within a year, Moshe Altberg decided that he would prefer to do the research and let Isaac go to court. It happened so slowly and naturally that it soon seemed as if it had always been that way.

Success brought more and more people to Peretz' door. During the day there were mostly people in trouble, looking for legal help. In the evenings and on Saturdays, however, young students and writers came to talk to him, to tell him their troubles, their dreams, and their problems with old-fashioned parents.

Sarah was upset by the steady stream of uninvited guests and wanted to discourage them from coming. Isaac, however, saw in each struggling student a picture of himself. He didn't have the heart to turn anyone away.

One Saturday, at lunchtime, there was a knock at the door. Sarah went to open it and found three boys, so shy that they each nudged the other to speak. Finally one said, "I have some poems to show Leib Peretz. I was sent by a friend of his in Warsaw. Forgive me for troubling . . ."

"There's no Leib Peretz here," she said angrily.

"Can't you read? Leon Perec lives here. A good day to you!"

Isaac heard her voice from the living room and came running. Sarah stood in front of the locked door. "I sent them away," she said. "It's too much! What is this house, a public square? Can't we even have a Sabbath meal in peace without some ragged students banging on the door? I didn't buy a new couch for beggarly, black-coated boys to sit on. I'm sick of all of them!"

Isaac angrily pulled the door open and ran after the boys. The neighbors were surprised to see him running through the street without a coat and with a napkin tucked into his belt.

He caught up with them in a few minutes and began to explain, "My wife wants to protect me, but I don't need protection. Come back to the house. I can see you've come a long way."

Sarah took four-year-old Lucien and went into the kitchen to eat. Isaac begged her to stay and see what the young men wanted, but she wouldn't. "You're driving me from my own house," she said in tears.

"You're driving yourself," said Isaac angrily.

"They'll spoil our new things I've waited so long to get," she cried.

"What do we need chairs for, if not to sit on?" Isaac said. "My door must be open to whoever knocks."

"You expect me to feed everyone. You lend money to everyone. No one pays you back."

"That's the way I want to live," said her husband, "with an open door and an open hand."

"Why can't you be like everyone else?" said Sarah.

"I can't close my door to the students with their little poems. I would have given anything to have someone to come to."

Isaac had his way. But Sarah wouldn't give in. He welcomed whoever came, but she locked herself in with Lucien and would not come out until the company had gone home. She heard her husband reading aloud in Russian or in Polish to his young friends. He read his own poems and stories and those that other young writers brought to him, while Sarah sulked in the kitchen with Lucien.

She would stand at the window and watch them leave; such an odd collection of people. Sometimes there were factory workers, sometimes young boys with earlocks and long black coats. When they left, Isaac would come in to her and

Lucien. He would pick up his son and kiss him, while Lucien tried to squirm away. "Sarah," Isaac pleaded, "how can I make you see what's going on? There's so much to teach. There are so many fools that have to be made wise and so many fanatics that have to learn good sense. What do these people who come here want of me? They want to find out where to study and what to learn. Give in, Sarah. Help me. Don't stand behind a locked door."

One Saturday afternoon, their living room was crowded with people. Some sat on the floor. Others perched on the window sills and the arms of chairs. Most of them were would-be writers who admired the stories and poems that Isaac had been publishing.

One young man excitedly said, "We should write only in Hebrew so that we can speak to Jews all over the world. Hebrew binds us together!"

"But we must know the language of the land in which we live," said Peretz. "If we forget Hebrew, we forget our religion, but we cut ourselves off from life and progress if we can't speak to the people around us. That's why I wrote my first poems in Polish."

"But Russian Jews don't know Polish. Nor do

the Jews of Germany or Austria. You'll lose them as an audience," said the young man.

"Yes," said Peretz. "If we really want to help and educate our own people we should write in Yiddish so that everyone can understand."

"We can't wait for people to learn other languages. Languages are neither good nor bad. Language is a tool that makes it possible for the educated to teach those who know less. If we want to teach our people, we should teach in Yiddish, the language they know."

"It's never been done," said the young man. "The scholars will laugh at us."

"But ordinary people will be able to read and learn," said an older man in work clothes. "Let the scholars laugh."

"What shall we write about?" asked another young man.

"You write what your heart tells you to write," said Peretz. "But remember that words aren't toys to play with for entertainment alone. Words are holy. They can teach and help. A bird sits on a branch and sings. A poet has to think of making the world better."

There was a long silence while they thought about what had been said and finally a well-dressed young fellow with a German accent said, "I like to read about nature, and love, and pretty girls. Don't you? Why can't we write for pleasure?"

"No one stops you," said Peretz. "It's just that we have so much to teach and explain to our people. When our problems are solved, we can do anything we like."

"But what about money?" the young man asked. "Wouldn't we make more money writing love stories in Polish than writing serious stories in Yiddish?"

"Money?" said Peretz. "If it's money you want then become a tailor, a shoemaker, be an honest baker . . ."

A rock came crashing through the window as he spoke. Then another and another. Sarah went to the door to see what was happening and a stone hit her forehead. Before she knew what was happening, two poorly dressed old men pushed their way into the house.

"Give my son back to me!" one shouted. "He doesn't belong here."

"Poisoning the minds of children," scolded the other.

They dragged their sons out by the ear,

threatened to beat them and Peretz too if they came back.

Some of the young people began to answer the old men, but Peretz hushed them. His eyes blazed with anger, but he held his tongue.

The students left, one by one, all ashamed of what had happened. Isaac bandaged Sarah's forehead and tried to comfort Lucien, who was weeping bitterly.

"Put the bad people in jail," said little Lucien.

Isaac took his son on his lap and rubbed his face against the soft four-year-old cheek. "Oh little one, jail won't teach them anything. They're poor, foolish people."

"But what will you do?" asked his wife. "You're a lawyer. At least you can force them to pay for the window and my broken head."

Isaac shrugged his shoulders.

"They could have killed someone," said Sarah. "Doesn't it matter to you?"

"Of course it matters. Do you think I asked them to throw stones?"

"Yes," she said. "You do. If you let anyone who knocks come into the house, what can you expect? Now you can see that I was right. Promise not to let these strangers in. Promise!"

Peretz didn't answer. He sat with his head in his hands.

"I can't promise," he said sadly. "I can't. Who are these bad people? The poorest of the poor. How can they pay for my window if they don't have anything to eat? Did you see the boys they dragged out? One a hunchback; the other, the one with a face the color of milk, had no soles in his shoes, just pieces of newspaper on the bottom and a few shreds of leather on top."

"This gives them permission to throw stones?"

"It doesn't give permission. They're fanatics because the world has treated them badly. Every change they've known has been for the worst. They're terrified because their children try to learn new ways. They have no hope, only fear. Have pity!"

"Have pity on me," said Sarah in tears. "Sabbath after Sabbath I spend in the kitchen or bedroom, listening to the gibberish in here."

"Why do you sit outside the door like a stranger? Why don't you join us? You say you're a modern woman. Behave like one!"

"Why can't you mind your own business? Take care of your practice and let other people alone.

I can't bear this any longer. If you won't promise to stop all this, I'll leave you."

"Sh," Isaac begged. "Lucien is listening."

"I don't care."

"I can't promise what you want."

"I'll leave in the morning."

Lucien began to cry. His father picked him up and put him to bed. Sarah began pulling her clothes out of the closet.

Isaac could not fall asleep until almost dawn. He had just dozed off when Lucien's crying woke him. Sarah was dressed in her best clothes. Her valise was packed. Her face was set stubbornly.

"Please take me along," Lucien begged. He held her skirt and cried.

"See a rabbi about a divorce," she said. "I can't bear it any longer. I'll leave Lucien with you. I want nothing to remind me of these years. I want them to pass like a bad dream. Good-by."

Tears dripped down her cheeks as she kissed her son and pulled him away from her.

"Who will look after him?" Isaac asked. "I can't take him to work with me."

"The Polish woman upstairs knows him and the house. She'll help you out. If you could only have tried to please me," she said at the door. "If I'm not dearer to you than the stream of beggars that pour into this house, then you can solve your own problems."

Isaac's heart was pounding. He picked Lucien up and held him close. "I can't do as you say, Sarah."

To Lucien he whispered, "Don't cry. She'll come back. What she wants is wrong. She'll think it over in a day or so and come back to us. You'll see, Lucien. She'll miss us and she'll come back."

9

The Busiest Man in Town

The days turned into weeks and the weeks into months. Sarah didn't come back. At the end of a year Sarah and Isaac were divorced. Isaac was the loneliest and the busiest man in Zamosh.

Every morning he took Lucien to school and then went on to his office or the courthouse. He brought Lucien back on his way home, gave him his supper, and put him to bed. Then he worked till the small hours of the night, not only on his law, but with community problems that he took upon himself.

It began with a school. When Isaac came to enroll Lucien in the Hebrew school, he was appalled to find that it had changed little from the time when he had gone. The room was still crowded and without proper light, desks, or chairs. The children had no play time. The teacher still kept a switch under his chair and the children were taught only Hebrew, the Bible, and the commentaries on the Bible. Isaac decided that he would convince a group of parents that it was time to modernize the school and its program.

Isaac dreamed of a school where children could learn Yiddish, Polish, and Russian as well as Hebrew. He wanted his son to study European history as well as Jewish history and he didn't want to neglect science and mathematics. The parents he met, however, could not agree with him. Some were afraid that education in Polish and science would weaken Jewish life. Some laughed at the idea of teaching Yiddish. Some thought that Hebrew could be forgotten. Without agreement nothing could be done.

Instead of a school for children, Peretz organized the first school for adults in Zamosh. He gave lectures on Jewish history and literature. There were classes in reading and writing for the women who had never had a chance to learn. The adult classes, of all things, led to the organization of a fire department.

124 ❧

One night, in the middle of his class, Peretz stopped, sniffed, and said, "Something's burning."

Some parents had left little children at home alone, asleep. Everyone ran home to make sure his family was safe.

One couple came home too late. Two children were lost!

"It's the lawyer's fault," said malicious people. "Women belong at home with their children, not in classes."

A white-faced Peretz came to comfort the grieving parents. "If we were punished," he said, "it's not for trying to learn. A town of 5,000 people must have a way to fight fire. We should have learned that years ago."

"Fire is sent by God," said an old man. "Nothing can fight fire!"

"Water fights fire in Warsaw and in Lemberg and in Vilna," said Peretz. "This is 1878 and it can be fought here too. We need a fire wagon and a team of horses. We need tanks for water, and hoses. Let the town buy such equipment and I will be the first to volunteer to be a fire fighter."

Isaac went to see the mayor the next day. He reminded him of the fire that once reached the town hall itself. The mayor agreed that Zamosh should have fire-fighting equipment. A few months later, the tower bell rang in the middle of the night. Isaac pulled on his clothes and ran. Friends met him at the new fire station. The shiny new wagon clattered through the streets and people turned in their beds and said, "Something's burning! There goes Peretz and his crazy wagon. Thank God!"

Little Lucien, however, was having a lonely time. The Polish woman who looked after him could not take his mother's place. He was growing up into a shy boy, who spoke very little. He kept hoping that his mother would come back and he became very angry when his father said that she wouldn't.

One evening the woman who took care of him fell asleep in her chair. Lucien tiptoed into his father's study. He took his father's notebooks and papers out of his desk, carried them to the kitchen, and pushed them into the stove.

Later that night, Lucien heard his father opening and closing drawers. He crept out of his bed and came into the study, barefoot, looking like a small, pale ghost.

"Don't look," he said, "I burned everything."

Peretz jumped! He stared at the small, angry face, partly like his own and partly like Sarah's.

"What do you mean, burned?" asked Peretz in disbelief.

"I burned your papers," Lucien repeated. "Now my mother can come back."

Peretz groaned. Months of work had been destroyed.

"Now you can spank me," said Lucien.

Peretz was down on his knees and a sad, angry father and a frightened little boy looked into each other's eyes.

"I've never spanked you," said Peretz. "How do you know I'll spank you?"

Lucien didn't answer.

"How could you do such a thing? You know you're never to touch anything here." Isaac put Lucien on his lap. "Please," he begged, "let's be friends. Let's help each other. I won't spank you, though you deserve to be spanked. Promise me that you won't hurt my work. I write for you as well as other people."

"I don't want you to," said Lucien.

"I must," said his father.

Lucien behaved badly at home and at school. He wouldn't obey and trusted no one. It was as if he were saying, "Who can I trust, if I can't trust my own mother?"

Isaac decided to send him to a modern private school where he would get more attention and discipline. He hated to send him away from home. He kept hoping that he would gain his confidence and become a real friend and father to him.

In spite of all his activities, Peretz was a lonely man. One night a friend scolded him. "You don't take care of yourself. You forget to eat and sleep. Take an afternoon off tomorrow and come with me. I'm driving down to the town of Lentsha. Come along for the ride."

"What do I want to go to Lentsha for?" asked Peretz.

"I'm going to buy some lumber from my cousin, Ringelheim. They have an inn there and the food is magnificent. For goodness sake, you've done me so many favors, let me take you to dinner once. I'll come for you at three. I won't take no for an answer."

The next day, promptly at three, Peretz settled back in the coach and was on his way to Lentsha.

"How did I get into this?" Peretz asked.

"A fine question! It seems to me," said his friend, "that in the last year you've managed to get involved with a school for adults, a fire department, a modern school for Jewish children, a Yiddish theater and dozens of students every Saturday afternoon. You have a successful law practice and I can't keep up with the stuff you've been publishing in the magazines. Relax, man! Stop running!"

Isaac laughed. When he leaned back on the leather seat, he realized how tired he was. He looked out of the tiny window and saw that the countryside was pleasant in August. There were cabbages, beets, and carrots in the field. He shut his eyes for a minute and fell asleep.

The coach stopped at the inn. Isaac shook his head to wake up and followed his friend to the door. "Go in and have a drink while I stop at the lumber yard down the road. I'll join you in a minute."

The inn seemed deserted. The bell on the door tinkled to announce Isaac's arrival.

"One moment, sir," called a pleasant voice in Polish. "I'll be right with you."

Peretz was surprised at the voice. It was too

young to be Mrs. Ringelheim and too cultured to be a servant girl. He watched the door to the kitchen curiously, to see who possessed such a pleasant voice. In a moment a young girl of about 20 came out to greet him. "I'm Helena Ringelheim," she said, "and you, you must be Isaac, Isaac Leib Peretz. Excuse me, the lawyer, Leon Perec . . . I'm happy to know you," she said, as she offered him her hand. "I'll bring some fish in a minute. What would you like to drink with it?"

Isaac shook his head in amazement. "How do you know who I am?"

"My cousin brought you here," she said. "He talks about you all the time. In fact, you're his only topic of conversation. We know all about your cases, your classes, your fire engine and your ideas about women voting. You have no secrets, and I'm talking too much. Let me bring some wine."

She disappeared behind the swinging door and Peretz took a deep breath. He had never seen such a girl; so much brown hair, and such bright laughing eyes.

Helena brought the wine and he begged her to sit down and talk with him.

"I'll tell you," said Peretz. "Your cousin is not a very bright fellow. To tell you all about me and me nothing about you is . . ."

"Don't blame him," she interrupted. "I'm the family problem child."

"What kind of problem could you be?"

"My father's problem! You see, he had no sons and since I was his only child he was determined to give me all the education one would give a whole family of children. Luckily I wasn't completely stupid. I studied Hebrew and Yiddish with a tutor and then he bought me a piano and a teacher from Warsaw and finally topped it all off with a convent school."

"Marvelous," said Peretz. "That's just how a bright girl should be treated. You chose your father wisely."

"I don't know," she said wistfully. "In sleepy old Lentsha, I'm a kind of freak. My old girl friends are more interested in babies than books and the men are afraid of an educated girl. I can cook and sew as well as any, but a man is afraid of a girl who knows more than he does."

"I'm not afraid," said Peretz with a twinkle in his eye.

Helena's father and cousin came in together. "I see you've met each other already," the cousin said innocently, as if he hadn't planned it all. "How's the wine?"

"Superb," said Peretz.

"How do you know?" said Helena. "You haven't tasted it."

"Play for us, Helena," the cousin asked.

"Not now," she pleaded.

"Why not now? How often do I hear a piano, and Peretz here knows nothing of music. Please."

The piano was in a corner of the room. Helena left the men and sat down to play. Peretz sat with his chin in his hand and listened.

"Chopin," said Mr. Ringelheim, "the greatest Polish musician. He once stopped in this very inn."

"Sh," said the cousin. "He doesn't hear a word you're saying. Helena has bewitched him."

"What was that about Helena?" asked Peretz.

The two men began to laugh. "I told you," said the cousin. "It was meant to be."

Helena stopped. "Why are you laughing? Have I done something wrong?"

"Wrong?" exclaimed Peretz indignantly. "It was beautiful, just beautiful."

"Can I come back soon?" Isaac asked when it was time to go.

"Please," said Helena with a flashing smile. "Come back soon."

When they were in the coach together, Helena's cousin turned to Isaac and said, "Well, what do you think of her?"

"I've never met such a delightful human being. Why didn't you tell me about her before?"

"I was afraid you wouldn't come if I told you. I was waiting for the proper time. I wanted to do you a favor in return for all the favors you've done for me. Well I've introduced you to Helena and we're even. The rest is up to you."

10

"I Live Again!"

Isaac did not get back to Lentsha as quickly as he hoped. But letters traveled back and forth regularly. By the time he saw Helena again her letters had made her his dearest friend. He carried her picture with him wherever he went and he poured out his heart to her in his own letters. At the end of one trying day, he wrote:

Dearest Helena,

I have seen so much sadness today. My heart is full and my head is full of a thousand bad dreams. How wonderful it would be if I had you here to talk to.

It's midnight. Zamosh is asleep, buried in the quiet starry night. But I cannot sleep. How thankful I am for you. My heart was so downcast. My whole life seemed like a bad dream and my head was lost in dark clouds. And now? The look from your bright eyes melted the ice around my heart. I think of you and it beats loudly for joy. The black clouds disappear and I'm filled with longing to see you. I live again! Because of you.

I will see you soon. Be well.

Love me,
Your Leon

Seven months after Isaac's first trip to Lentsha, he returned to the inn for a wedding. It was the 17th of February, 1878, a cold, dreary, winter day. The guests, however, forgot the ice and snow when they looked at the bride and groom. Helena, with her crown of dark hair, was as happy and beautiful a bride as they had ever seen. Isaac's eyes glistened and he couldn't stop smiling.

Isaac permitted himself the luxury of a honeymoon trip for a week. Then Helena came home with him to Zamosh. She became part of Isaac's life quickly. After a few months he couldn't imagine life without her. His friends became her friends. The students adored her. She was a gracious hostess. She came to her husband's classes and taught a few herself.

Helena devoted herself to Isaac and his interests. She organized a group of women to provide free lunches for the poor Talmud Torah children. She and Isaac persuaded some businessmen to build a hospital that would give free medical care to those who couldn't pay for it. They both worked to modernize the school in Zamosh.

Helena and Isaac also spent many uncomfortable hours with Lucien. They tried everything they could think of to make him happy. But he was surrounded by a wall of shyness and anger. He couldn't seem to recover from his distrust.

One evening, however, Isaac came home with news that made him forget his personal problems.

"A new decree from Petersburg," he said to Helena as he took off his coat. "The worst in 20 years! Alexander II has decided that Russia must go back to its old ways. Gorchakov, the Russian minister, at the Congress of Berlin made the announcement for the whole world to hear."

"I don't understand," said Helena. "What has this to do with us?"

"In Berlin, statesmen from every country in the world agreed that Jews must have the same laws and the same freedom as other people. Everyone agrees, but not Gorchakov."

"I studied about Alexander in school," Helena said indignantly. "Isn't he the one who gave forty million serfs their freedom? He's the one who gave Jews permission to attend the universities and stopped taking little children into the army. I know from my uncle in Petersburg that Alexander II was the first to welcome Jewish merchants, artisans, and mechanics into the cities. Is it the same Alexander?"

"The same Alexander, and it's all over. All Jewish schools are closed. Jewish boys will go into the army five years before the rest of the population and cannot advance beyond private. Merchants and businessmen are losing everything."

"But why? It makes no sense," said Helena.

"It makes sense to him. He's disappointed in his own accomplishments and ready to blame everyone but himself. He gave his peasants freedom, but no money and no education. Instead of being satisfied, they want more than he gave them. They take revenge in riots, and in attempts at revolution. Meanwhile we have disappointed him even more. He thought that Jews would convert and forget their religion and their ways if he let them into the universities. But they remained Jews. Now he invites the peasants to burn their houses, their synagogues. . . . Sense? Justice?"

"What will people do?" Helena asked. "Can we help them?"

"They've already begun running away. Those who remember the old days are the first."

"Do you think we'll have trouble here?"

"Russia is master. A pebble thrown into the pond at Petersburg sends ripples all the way to Zamosh."

"What can we do?"

"People must know what's happening," said Isaac. "We must stand together. We can help the refugees. We can't behave like meek little lambs waiting for the slaughter. If we can't fight, we can pray. The rabbis can set aside a day for prayer and fasting. We must do something to show that we're united and not ready for conversion or destruction."

Isaac went to all the rabbis in the city. At the German synagogue the rabbi looked at him as if he were a madman. "The only sensible thing is to be quiet and not attract attention. We mustn't look for trouble," he said.

He went from the large synagogue where the wealthy prayed to the humble cottage where the Chasidim studied and sang. The rabbi listened patiently and said, "Young man, we are in the Almighty's hands. Whatever He wishes, He will do with us."

In the familiar synagogue, where Isaac had come since he was a little boy, the rabbi was too frightened to speak with him. "I've seen the refugees," he said. "They're running with just the clothes on their backs as in the old bad days."

On the following Sabbath, however, Isaac stood up when the services were over and spoke about the decree from Petersburg. He reminded them of Hillel's words, "If I don't look out for myself, who will look out for me? But if I care only for myself, then what am I?" The rabbi tried to silence him, but Isaac proposed a day of fasting so that food could be sent to those who had lost their homes. He pleaded for a day of prayer and protest.

"What good will it do?" one man grumbled.

"He's right," shouted another. "We mustn't

bow our heads. We must stand up for our rights and those of our brothers."

"Our people were the first to teach the world about freedom," said an old man, "and the last to receive the blessing of freedom."

Isaac's announcement in the synagogue was printed in the Yiddish newspaper. The papers were passed from hand to hand.

On the appointed day, the Russian soldiers patrolled an empty market place. Men and women in Sabbath clothes gathered in the synagogue. The collection boxes filled up with coins.

It took all morning for the Russian authorities in Zamosh to realize what it was about. When they did, they were still bewildered. "Why do they care in Zamosh for what goes on in Petersburg?" they asked each other.

The Jews of Zamosh, however, were strengthened by a day of fasting. They knew that they could unite to help each other. They knew, too, that the lawyer, Peretz, would speak for them when they were too frightened to speak for themselves.

THE CHIEF OF POLICE

11

Back to Warsaw!

The people of Zamosh waited anxiously for news from Petersburg. There were riots and pogroms in the Russian cities and villages and the trains were always filled with refugees. Life in Zamosh, however, remained the same.

Isaac's law practice grew steadily more successful. Even the Polish gentry came for his help. He still wrote stories and articles for Polish, Yiddish, and Hebrew journals. But he couldn't relax. He and Helena were very happy together. They had enough money. Their only sadness was that they had no children and Lucien was never at ease with his father or Helena. They tried to make up for their lack of children by looking after others' children. Sometimes Peretz behaved as if all the little ones in the Talmud Torah school were his responsibility.

Peretz came home late one evening. Helena could tell by the slam of the door that something was wrong.

"I went to Markowsky's funeral today," he said as he took off his coat.

"Such a funeral!" Isaac said. "There were more than a hundred carriages. All the dignitaries! All the proper people honoring the richest man in the city."

"But what's wrong with it?" Helena asked.

"There were three carriages filled with flowers alone. A mountain of flowers that the frost will kill by morning."

"His friends have money to throw away," Helena said. "Why are you so angry?"

"I'll tell you exactly how it was," Isaac said slowly. "First there was the hearse and then the carriages with flowers, and then a long line of carriages with top hats and fur-lined coats and warm rugs over good leather boots. At the end of this procession came the children from the orphanage and the Talmud Torah school, dragging their little feet in torn shoes. They were shivering in the March wind. A hundred running noses and a thousand frozen fingers while our great men tucked the robes under their knees. . . . The price of the flowers could have bought shoes and jackets for the whole orphanage!"

"Why did they bring them?" Helena asked.

"Markowsky built the orphanage and donated the buildings for the school, since they were too broken down for even his business to use. His wife thought the children should honor their benefactor. How many times did I beg him to repair a window, or buy some clothes or books? He was sure the poor children were so lucky to be under his care. He couldn't see why they needed shoes too."

"You see too much," Helena said.

"I'll write about it for the newspaper," Isaac said. "People have no sense of values. Stupidity and selfishness are our worst enemies."

The article appeared in the newspaper a few days later and Peretz was overwhelmed by the letters his readers sent him. Most of them praised him for his courage but a few argued that he had no right to criticize the richest men in the city.

Helena watched while he opened his mail. Peretz opened letter after letter, sometimes smiling, sometimes scowling. At the bottom of the heap was an official-looking envelope from Petersburg. He expected a tax collector's form or some notice to lawyers. Helena was frightened by the expression on his face. He turned pale, then red, and then pale again.

"There must be some mistake." He handed her the letter. There were only a few lines saying:

We have been informed of your revolutionary activity and hearby revoke your license to practice law anywhere in Poland or Russia. There will be a jail sentence for any violation. Your office is in the hands of the police.

Isaac went to the courthouse immediately. The judge agreed to inquire for him, but he gave him no encouragement. From the courthouse, Isaac went to the chief of police.

"There's no mistake," the police chief said. "We're searching the town for revolutionary books and wherever we found what we're looking for, we also found your little books and your articles cut out of newspapers and magazines."

"Did you read any of my little books?" Peretz asked furiously. "Read them and you'll see I couldn't possibly be a revolutionary."

"It's not my job to read the books. It's enough that I have to hunt them down and get rid of them."

"I'll go to Petersburg," said Isaac. "I can prove that I've never had anything to do with the revolutionaries."

"Save your money," said the police chief.

The next months were like a bad dream from which Isaac could not awaken. Long after he was ready to give up, Helena and Moshe Altberg insisted that he keep fighting for permission to continue his law practice.

"There's no one to talk to," said Isaac. "The Russian government is afraid that the people will revolt. The laws get more strict every day and the people get angrier every day. Who is interested in me and my problems when such a storm is brewing?"

Peretz used up his money in a few months of idleness. He wrote to Sholom Aleichem, a famous Yiddish writer, and said: ". . . I never planned or dreamed to earn money by writing. I always said that Torah wasn't a spade to dig with. But today I send you some manuscripts, hoping that they can earn me some money. I have no choice."

Sholom Aleichem wrote back to say, "Come to Warsaw. You have more friends than you think. Meanwhile, I will find a place for your manuscripts. . . ."

Sixteen years before, a frightened young Peretz came to Warsaw to study. He returned as a well-known writer, with more friends than he knew he had.

Lucien joined his father in Warsaw. There was no longer enough money to pay for his schooling. He came home unexpectedly to a room full of people. His father was telling a story in Yiddish. Lucien slipped into the kitchen where Helena was fixing tea for her guests.

She put everything down and rushed to throw her arms around him.

"Don't be so pleased to see me," Lucien said unkindly. "I'm not pleased to be here. Why did he have to ruin everything? He should have held onto his practice."

"Lucien, he did everything possible," Helena said angrily.

"If he had minded his own business, I'd be back

in school now. If he weren't such a show-off, he'd have his nice little old office this minute."

"You've been here only two minutes," Helena begged. "Let's not quarrel."

"I'm not quarreling," Lucien said. "I just can't see how you stand the band of gypsies that follow him around. Doesn't he ever get tired of hearing himself talk?"

"Please go, Lucien, if that's what you've come for." Helena said. "Don't hurt him."

Lucien joined the young people in the living room. Isaac had just returned from a visit to many provinces around Warsaw. He was working for the Warsaw Community Council and was a member of a statistical expedition. A wealthy banker interested in helping Polish Jews wanted to find out how they lived. Peretz and a few other research men traveled from town to town, gathering information. The young people in the living room were fascinated by Peretz' report of his travels. He came home not with dry statistics but with wonderful descriptions of how men and women lived, how children studied and played, the songs they sang, the food they ate. Instead of writing his information in lists and tables, he wrote down his adventures in story form. He was reading aloud from one of the stories when Lucien came in.

When Peretz finished, everyone began to talk at once. A young man sitting in front of Lucien grabbed his arm and said, "I read every word the man writes. What did you think of his last article?"

"I didn't read it," Lucien said.

"I have a copy of it. You must read it."

"I couldn't be bothered," said Lucien.

"Bothered," the boy said angrily. "What's wrong with you, anyway?"

"I think Yiddish should be abolished," Lucien said loudly. "We're Poles and we should speak only Polish."

"What do you come here for?" the stranger said. "You won't find anyone who agrees with you."

"I don't come here," Lucien said. "I live here."

"Who are you?" the boy asked.

"I'm Lucien Perec, son of the one-time lawyer, Leon Perec, who lets his friends call him Isaac, Isaac Leib Peretz."

"What a pity," the young man said. "I'd give anything to trade places with you."

Suddenly Peretz' voice rang above the others.

He was answering a question that they hadn't heard. He said, "Look, friend, a man without belief in God, in the world, and in idealism cannot live."

"How old-fashioned, father," Lucien called out. "Science will take the world over. We don't need God any more."

"Not so fast, son," Peretz said gently. "I've read more psychology than you. The Chasidic rabbis in the smallest, most dilapidated towns know more about human nature than your best modern research man." Peretz moved to put his arm around Lucien's shoulders. "Welcome home," he said softly.

Lucien shrugged to show his indifference. His father said, "Maybe it's hard for you to believe in the wisdom the rabbis have accumulated in over three thousand years, but it will be harder to spend your life in doubt. The hardest thing in the world is to live without knowing what you believe."

Helena brought the tea. She offered some to Lucien and whispered, "Please behave yourself!"

He smiled. "Don't worry. He's already given me my lecture for today. I feel quite at home."

Lucien waited for the guests to leave before he

told his father, "I've only come back because I ran out of money and my tuition wasn't paid. I won't stay any longer than I have to."

Peretz puffed at his cigar and drummed his fingers on the table as if it would help him be patient. "Lucien," he said, "these are bad times. I may never earn much money again. I have a job with the Jewish Community Council. It doesn't pay well. I have to teach and lecture at night so that the rent can be paid. The easy times are over!"

Lucien said peevishly, "I like easy times."

"Go, then," Peretz shouted angrily. "If you can't share what we have, go!"

Lucien grabbed the valise that he had left at the door and ran out of the house.

Peretz jumped up as if to catch him, but Helena held him back. "Let him come of his own accord," she begged.

"I tried so hard," Peretz said bitterly. "I can't accept it. . . . Thousands of people trust me and respect me . . . but not my only son."

12

The End of a Century

By the time the year 1899 drew to a close, Peretz'
name was familiar to all Yiddish-speaking Jews in
Europe and in America. His stories were translated into Polish, German, Russian, and English.
He wrote for almost all the Yiddish magazines and
newspapers and had half a dozen pen names. It
did not matter that he signed his pieces, "The
Bee," or "Mr. Accident." Everyone knew who it
was.

His words traveled around the world, but his
personality belonged to Warsaw. He was the
busiest lecturer in the city.

One night, Helena glanced at his calendar and

groaned. Isaac had speaking engagements for ten nights in a row.

"When will you get some sleep?" she scolded. "You have to stop and rest a little."

"How can I disappoint them? It's so hard to say no," Isaac said.

Helena read aloud, looking for one that she could cross off the list. "The Writers Association, The Young Zionists, Public Health Department, Teachers' Association, Synagogue Brotherhood, The Lovers of Zion, The Theater Guild, The Jewish Workers' Association, The Polish Socialist Party . . . not there," Helena begged. "Every time they meet, there's trouble."

"I'm going to read one of my stories," Peretz said. "What can happen?"

"You don't agree with them. Why should you endanger yourself?"

"Danger?" Peretz shrugged. "I suppose I want to talk to them just because I disagree with them. It's a wonder they asked me. We'll see what happens."

"Let them see without you," Helena pleaded.

"It's a fund-raising meeting to help the families whose men are out of work. How can I refuse them?"

The day before the meeting, however, the chairman came to see Peretz. "The police may break up our meeting tonight. I wanted you to know. You're under no obligation to come."

Isaac looked at his guest thoughtfully, noticing his rough clothes, his worn cap, and his worried, tired face. "Tell me, friend, are you going to the meeting tonight?"

"I must," the man said. "I'm the chairman."

"If it's safe enough for you, then it'll be safe enough for me. Don't worry! Perhaps the police will think better of breaking up your meeting after they hear me. Perhaps you'll be sorry you asked me."

"Never," said the man earnestly. "Thank you. We'll take every precaution, I give you my word."

The next night, Peretz came into a large meeting hall. The room was packed with people. Those who couldn't fit into the main hall were standing in the entrance hall, where they could hear if they couldn't see. A few stood on guard outside so that Peretz could be warned and escape if the police should come.

Peretz stood up to speak and there wasn't a sound. It was a pity that Helena didn't come to hear him. She was worried about his tiredness, but the excitement of an eager audience brought a flush to his cheeks. His eyes sparkled. He had smiles for everyone.

"Why am I here, friends? I am not a member of your party. But we are all opposed to what is old and decayed. We hope for a better world. We must be friends. Let us remember that searching and striving are more important than finding. Thinking is more important than knowing. The future is more exciting than the past.

"My heart is with you. Every man *should* have what he needs. Everyone should be free to choose his way of life and free to find his work. When you clench your fists at those who would keep the world back, I pray that God gives you the strength to succeed. And yet . . . I'm afraid for you. You want people to march like an army— but humanity isn't an army. The strong are the leaders. The sensitive feel deeply. The proud grow tall. Be careful, friends. Be sure that you don't cut down the cedar trees to keep them from growing taller than the grass."

There was not a sound from the audience. It was not what they had come to hear, but they listened respectfully. The people who flocked to hear him knew that he might make them angry. He might make them laugh, but he would also force them to think.

He suddenly changed his role. He stopped teaching and began to tell a story as only he could tell it. It was a fairy tale for grownups, the story called "The Pious Cat."

The audience listened as eagerly as children at a story hour and broke into applause when the tale was done. A long line of men and women came to shake his hand before they left the hall. Peretz joked with the chairman. "How you worried for nothing," he said. "You and my wife, a pair of old ladies."

"Better to be frightened than beaten," the chairman answered. "I won't relax till you're safe at home."

Four men, in working clothes like everyone else, remained at the end of the line, muttering and whispering to each other. When there were about a dozen people left in the hall, one shouted, "Now!"

They drew guns from their jackets and surrounded the people left in the room.

"The best for last," one said in Russian.

The warning was not in vain. The czarist police

had raided the meeting and were ready to take the leaders to jail. All meetings of workers were illegal because of the fear of revolution.

Everyone protested that Peretz was innocent. "He was a guest," the chairman shouted. "He has nothing to do with us. Let him go!"

"Let him choose his friends more carefully," the police said as they pushed him into the waiting wagon with the other men.

Peretz was paid for one night's lecture with three months in jail. Though he wrote some of his best stories during those few months, he came home weak and sick.

Peretz' friends were always amazed by his incredible energy and youthful enthusiasm. Only Helena knew how his public appearances exhausted him. She worried because he smoked too many cigarettes and drank too much black coffee. She begged him to rest, but he was too tense to waste time sleeping.

On Peretz' fiftieth birthday, his friends planned a surprise for him, the biggest banquet ever held. So many people begged to come that it took three days to complete the celebration. Telegrams and congratulations came from all over the world.

The great and famous writers and the most important people in the community sat at the head of the banquet table. The young people who were constant guests in Isaac's home sat at the back. They had taken up a collection and bought him a golden pen for the occasion. Isaac impulsively left the head table and joined the young people.

"You must organize a school for us," one of his young friends begged.

"Never," Peretz said with a smile. "Poetry comes from the heart, not from a school."

"Lead us then," said another writer, "and we'll follow you."

"No," Peretz said quickly. "Don't follow me. Blaze a new path. Find new ways and new roads."

On the last night of the anniversary celebrations, Isaac and a few of his closest friends sat in his living room, talking about the exciting days that had passed. Helena answered a knock at the door. There were two men in work clothes in the hallway, asking for Peretz. They refused to come in.

Isaac left his guests and went to the door. He

came back in a moment with a flaming face. He had a small package in his hand that he gave to his friend Dyneson to open.

Dyneson opened it cautiously. There were two books. One was so old it was falling to pieces. The pages were torn and smeared. The cover was ripped to shreds. The other was brand new, edged in gold with a red leather cover, but full of blank pages.

"It's the first book you ever published," Dyneson said. "Where did it come from?"

The note slipped out and explained everything. It said,

Greetings from your friends of the Revolutionary Party. Your first book has been hidden many times; it has been read by hundreds of people; it has been arrested and taken to jail more times than we can count. We send it back to you with a blank volume. May you fill it in the next twenty-five years with as exciting words and thoughts as you have given us in the past twenty-five years.

"Idiots," said Isaac's friend and publisher, Dyneson. "Haven't they caused you enough trouble already?" He took a match from his pocket. In everyone's sight, he burned the note so that the prying police would never find it. He wanted to burn the book too, but Peretz held it tightly. "This I will save," he said.

The Golden Anniversary began ten of the most productive years of Peretz' life. He had his finger in all Jewish affairs and he wrote constantly. Legends and folk tales that he collected in his travels or remembered as far back as Reb Pinkhes in Shebreshin came to life in stories about the Chasidim. He seemed to understand them better than they understood themselves.

When there were celebrations, Peretz was there. When there was trouble, he was the first to come to help and comfort. If friends were gold pieces, Peretz would have been a millionaire, but he had very little money. He wanted to visit America and Palestine, but he could never afford the journey. Instead, he was welcomed in all the cities of Poland, Russia, Latvia, and Galicia. When he came back to Zamosh, the whole town gathered in the square to greet him. In the excitement, the horses pulled away from his carriage. A few strong young men jumped up and pulled the coach themselves.

When the ten years passed, however, a way of life passed with them. In 1912 a storm that had been brewing for many years broke upon the Jews of Poland. The trouble Peretz had feared from Petersburg in 1878 reached Warsaw 34 years later, when the day of protest Isaac had organized in Zamosh was long forgotten and it was too late for another.

Peretz opened his door one morning, went out, and then turned to see what caught his eye. On his door in black letters, was written, "Dirty Jew!"

Helena came to see why he turned back and gasped. "Let me clean it off," she said fearfully.

"No," said Peretz sadly. "Let those who believe in the great Polish culture see it. Let them be ashamed."

That morning the Polish press announced a Jewish boycott. Polish patriots paraded in front of Jewish shops and businesses, forbidding people to buy. Homes and synagogues were burned. Jewish children were expelled from school and government employees were fired. The Jewish neighborhoods were filled with frightened people, asking, "Why?"

Just as they began to take freedom and citizenship for granted, a new movement swept their rights away. Poland, under Russian domination, lost interest in the right of every person to live and worship as he pleased. The nation's right to rule itself became more urgent. The Jewish community was told that it didn't belong in the new nation. Even the Jews who gave up their religion, their customs, and their community were considered strangers in the land in which they were born.

Most of the people who crowded into Isaac's office during the days of the boycott came for help in running away to America, to England, France, or Germany. The most unhappy Jews of all were those who considered themselves Polish patriots. They spoke only Polish, educated their children in Polish schools, and lived and worked as Poles. They could not bear to have their Polish friends attack them without reason.

Peretz tried to fight the fear and panic that spread like wildfire. He gathered around him other proud and angry Jewish leaders who were not afraid to speak out against their government.

"Throw away your fear," Peretz begged. "Fear is no friend. We must be stubborn and organize ourselves. The boycott cannot go on forever. We must live through it and win. Poland will have to accept us as we are, and give us back our freedom. We want to be helpers in Poland, but we won't part with our beliefs and our ways. We believe in equality and fight for equality!"

Some Jewish leaders shook their heads at his words. "We will never win," they said. "Poland will never change. We must run away."

Others said, "We cannot run. We must give in and accept the religion of Poland. If we want to be safe, we must forget our tradition and history."

Isaac answered both groups with the same, "No!" He insisted that Poland could change. He believed that the anti-Semitism was a sickness that had been caught from the Russian government in Petersburg and that Poland could recover. "But it must never look back," he said, "or it will turn to stone like Lot's wife."

The leaders quarreled, but ordinary people read Peretz' articles in the Yiddish newspapers and were encouraged by them. He was the only one who offered hope and perspective and they cherished his words and thoughts.

There were times, however, when even Peretz was terrified and exhausted from the strain of working and fighting. One evening, on his way home from a discouraging meeting, he looked at a man opposite him in the coach and recognized a familiar face. It was Janek, an old friend who had helped him with Michel Fidler's books. He wanted to throw his arms around him, but hesitated, not knowing whether his friend would recognize him or want to speak to him. Janek stared, wrinkled his brow, and shrieked, "Isaac." In a moment, years were erased. They had so much to tell each other. For the first time, Isaac heard a Pole deplore the turn of events. "An epidemic of cruelty has caught our country," Janek said. "I worry so much about you and others like you. Every time I pick up the paper I'm ashamed of my countrymen."

Isaac said good-by to his old friend in better spirits. With a few sympathetic words, Janek convinced him that he was not alone. There were people in other walks of life that agreed with him and had hopes for a better future.

At home, a surprise awaited Isaac. When he came to his door, he heard a baby cry. He wondered what guest Helena was entertaining.

Lucien was waiting for him. With him was his wife and an infant. Isaac had not seen his son in ten years. He had never met his daughter-in-law or the baby.

Lucien had changed very little. He was still moody and disagreeable. He was ill. He had lost his job because of the boycott and had no money.

"You can stay here as long as you need to," said Peretz.

"Of course," echoed Helena, who already held the baby in her lap.

Their daughter-in-law kissed them both and thanked him. "I made Lucien come," she said. "He was ashamed to come, but I was afraid we'd starve if we didn't come to you."

Lucien was forced to depend upon his father, but he still had his old need to quarrel with him. He glanced at the newspapers with his father's articles and said, "So you still can't be quiet? You still have to embarrass everybody."

"It's no time to be quiet," Peretz answered. "We have ideals. The world will come to us to learn about morality. You'll see."

Lucien laughed. "I can imagine it, Papa. The Japanese will no doubt throw away their kimonos and chopsticks and come to eat matzoh and noodle pudding with us."

"Yes," said his father earnestly. "When modern

men get tired of their little gods, they will look into our books and find the ideals and the great dreams that make life possible."

"No," said Lucien, "they'll be freethinkers like me. They won't want your old books."

"I'm not afraid of freethinkers," said his father. "The person who has questions and is uncertain is my friend. Understand, Lucien! Only big angels fall out of heaven. The little ones are afraid. But I don't like your 'No.' It's dramatic to be a freethinker and to be uncertain all the time. But to be sure that you believe in nothing, and to be sure that there is nothing to believe is stupid."

Lucien left his father's house as abruptly as he came. He didn't say good-by or tell them where he was going with his wife and child. To Helena, however, he admitted, "I can't stand his sermons. Maybe he's right, but I'm not strong enough to spend my life fighting for ideals. I want to be like everyone else. I don't want nasty words scribbled on my door. I don't want to be boycotted. I don't care to be a Jew if it brings me so much trouble."

Isaac and Helena never saw him or heard from him again.

They had no time for hurt feelings. The boycott continued and terrible news from Russia added to the problems. Refugees from the riots and pogroms began pouring into Warsaw. Isaac's phone rang all day. His door was never shut. The Russian government stopped all publishing of newspapers and magazines. The magazine offices became a headquarters for refugees.

Hundreds of exhausted people came to Warsaw every day. They came on foot, half-naked, bare-foot, hungry, and frozen. They needed clothes, food, shelter, and some hope that they could live through their disaster. Isaac spent his days on the phone begging for places to sleep, for food, and money. He gave half of his salary to the refugee fund and turned the Jewish community hall, where he had lectured so often, into a dormitory. Peretz would stand at his office and look down from the balcony at the hall full of baggage, bed-clothes, utensils, and clothes. Old grandmothers who could not take another step sat on the bundles. Homeless children slept on the floor. Peretz would look down without saying a word. It was a pitiful sight. He watched it as if he were turned to stone. When he came home he could neither eat nor sleep.

One afternoon the director of the Jewish Aid Organization asked Peretz to help him at the railroad station, where a new group of refugees was arriving. Money had been sent from America to help them, but there were many difficult decisions to be made. The two men watched a whole town of people who had been driven from their homes. Suddenly Isaac gasped and held onto the wall. He had had a shock. He left the director and limped home in great pain.

Two days later, however, he was back at work. Helena was furious with him. His doctor insisted that he go away to rest. But World War I had already begun. Helena tried to make arrangements for Peretz to leave Warsaw for a few days, but only succeeded in being unable to return to Warsaw herself. Soldiers filled the trains. Civilians had to wait. She went away for a few hours and didn't come back for three days.

While Helena was away, Peretz gave away all the food she had left in the house. There was an auction to raise money for the refugees. He donated most of the furniture and pictures in his house.

Helena came home and wept. She realized how

❧ 171

much the last two years had changed him. The youthful, exuberant Peretz was no more. In his place sat a tired old man with drooping mustache and sunken cheeks. His flashing eyes were at once frightened and resigned.

"Don't cry about the furniture," he begged. "It just seemed that we didn't need it any longer."

"I'm not crying about the furniture," she said.

"There's nothing to eat but black bread. There are so many children coming to the community hall and all of them are hungry. I couldn't keep the cans in the cupboard while children were going hungry."

"Of course," said Helena. "Your jacket's so big. I'll have to take your clothes in. . . . Did you give the sewing machine away?"

"I only lent it to someone. I'll soon remember. It was for the kindergarten."

"What kindergarten?"

"Dyneson and I have organized a kindergarten, just the other day. We have a house at 7 Gensha Street and a few teachers already. It's absolutely necessary. The streets are full of lost, orphaned children. How can we let them wander about, hungry and frightened, like alley cats?"

"You didn't even tell me . . ."

"You were away, dearest. Now you can help. We've already decided that it must be a Yiddish-speaking school. And we have a motto. There will be a large sign over the door and it will say, 'Be yourself! Be yourself to the fullest!'"

Helena turned away so that he wouldn't see the tears in her eyes.

The school grew just as he planned. A few months later he was visiting it regularly. He liked to come to tell stories, to write poems and songs for the children. He collected his children's stories in a special book. When it was published in America, he received some money. But in his usual fashion, he returned it. "Buy books for your children," he wrote to the school that had bought his books. "These can be my present to your children in America."

All of Isaac's friends worried about him, but no one could keep him from working. During the winter of 1914, he planned a history of Jewish life in wartime. "We must write our own history," he said to Dyneson, "and not leave it for others to do."

The winter passed, as even the worst dream passes. Millions of men were fighting each other in trenches that stretched across Europe for hundreds of miles. Poland was caught in the fighting between the Russian and the German armies. The boycott was forgotten as greater problems took its place. Peretz found it harder and harder even to look at the paper. "All the blossoms in our garden have been destroyed," he said sadly. Caring for the children became his only pleasure.

On a Saturday, the third of the intermediate days of Passover, Peretz awoke at six o'clock and started to work at his desk. He looked at some papers for a few minutes, then opened the window. He went back to his desk, picked up his pen, and put his head down on his arms. On the paper in front of him was a poem he had begun the day before. It said:

Still, still,
Thanks he will . . .

and no more. Helena found him when she woke and went to call him to breakfast.

Before the day was over hundreds of friends and strangers came to the house for a last farewell. The students he had loved and helped stood guard at the door and let the guests in 15 at a time.

On Sunday 150,000 people came to his funeral. A long human chain stretched throughout the city. Old men and students, pious Chasidim in long black coats and intellectuals in European clothes. Every Jewish organization sent its representatives. His coffin was carried all the way on the shoulders of the young men who had been devoted to him all his life. It was a silent parade, disturbed only by the Polish carriages that tried to break through it. The police refused to stop traffic in his honor. But the march couldn't be stopped. It was as if all the people remembered hearing Peretz say, "Don't stop! Go on! The best road hasn't been found. Don't accept too little! Life can and must be better!"

It was a cloudy day, but when they arrived at the cemetery, the sun came out suddenly, bathing the people in a golden light, as if even the sun wanted to make its last farewell.

Covenant Books

Stories of Jewish Men and Women
To Inspire and Instruct Young People

Covenant Books are a new and fascinating series designed to take young people, eleven to fifteen years of age, on an adventurous expedition into the realms of Jewish experience. This is achieved by means of colorful biographies of Jewish personalities—prophets, rabbis, martyrs, philanthropists, writers, scientists—each representative of the many facets of a great tradition. Interestingly written, with a wealth of background information, Covenant Books will stimulate the young reader's interest in his cultural heritage and prove a rewarding spiritual experience.

SILVERSMITH OF OLD NEW YORK: MYER MYERS *by William Wise*. A dramatic story of old New York and of the ambitions and struggles of one of the first great Jewish artists and patriots of Colonial Times.

BORDER HAWK: AUGUST BONDI *by Lloyd Alexander*. The story of an immigrant from Vienna in 1849, who found opportunities for continuing his idealistic struggles for freedom in his new home as he had struggled in the old.

THE WORLD OF JO DAVIDSON *by Lois Harris Kuhn*. Jo Davidson lifted himself from the slums of New York's lower East Side to become one of the greatest sculptors the world has ever known. This is the inspiring story of how he did it and of his meetings and friendship with many of the great people of the world.

JUBAL AND THE PROPHET *by Frieda Clark Hyman*. The story of Jubal, the son of an important priest in the First Temple; and of the prophet Jeremiah during the time that Jerusalem was under the siege of the Babylonian army. A story filled with constant action and human as well as spiritual emotion.

(*continued*)

THE UNCOMMON SOLDIER: MAJOR ALFRED MORDECAI *by Robert D. Abrahams.* At the outbreak of the Civil War Alfred Mordecai, a Southerner and a career officer in the U.S. Army, was the husband of a Philadelphia girl whose sympathies were with the North, and the father of a cadet at West Point. How he faced the dilemma of the war between the states is the theme of this true story of an American Jewish hero.

THE VOICE OF LIBERTY: THE STORY OF EMMA LAZARUS *by Eve Merriam.* Emma Lazarus spent her brief life writing magazine articles and poetry, fighting for the welfare of the immigrants ("Give me your tired, your poor"), the establishment of a Jewish nation in Palestine, and for the rights of peoples everywhere. Her most famous poem, "The New Colossus," is engraved on the Statue of Liberty.

KEYS TO A MAGIC DOOR: ISAAC LEIB PERETZ *by Sylvia Rothchild.* In 1863, in the Polish town of Zamosh, eleven-year-old Isaac Leib Peretz had the reputation of being the smartest and the wildest boy in town. He learned to read when he was three years old and knew more than his teachers when he was ten. His escapades, however, unnerved his parents, teachers, and friends. However the wild young genius grew up to be a great writer, teacher, lawyer, and community leader, an inspiration to his own time and to our own.

ABOAB: THE FIRST RABBI OF THE AMERICAS *by Emily Hahn.* In 1641 the Dutch moved into Récife, a colony in Brazil which they had taken from the Portuguese, and the Jews of Amsterdam decided to send Rabbi Aboab with a group of pioneers to head the first New World synagogue. After 13 adventurous years the Dutch were finally defeated by the Portuguese, and Isaac Aboab returned to Amsterdam. But 23 of the community went to New Amsterdam, a Dutch colony in North America, and there they founded a congregation in the city that became New York.